Endorsements for the new 2009 Healing Touch Guidebook

"*Healing Touch Guidebook* provides Janet Mentgen's vision for a healing modality that is now part of the recognized field of Energy Medicine. Dorothea is a master communicator as well as a wise, founding elder in the practice of energy therapies. The work is written from a comprehensive body-mind-spirit perspective that expands the existing science and art of Healing Touch. It offers new insights for practice, education, and research with guidelines to bring the modality to the forefront of healthcare."

> —**Barbara Dossey,** PhD, RN, AHN-BC, FAAN, Author, *Holistic Nursing: A handbook for practice* (5th ed) and *Florence Nightingale: Mystic visionary, healer.*

"The new *Healing Touch Guidebook,* written with a deep spirit of love and service that sings from each page, provides a clear and up-to-date overview of the Healing Touch Program and its many applications in creating a true, healing healthcare system."

> —**Janet F. Quinn**, PhD, RN, FAAN, author of *I Am a Woman Finding My Voice*

"Much more than a comprehensive how-to book, the new *Healing Touch Guidebook* gives insight into the science and nature of the human biofield. Healing Touch is brought to life in vivid real-life cases exemplifying the principles and practices in the stage-wise progression towards mastery that culminates in the self-care and spiritual development of the HT practitioner. This is a true sourcebook and sets the standard in the field."

> —**Gregory Nicosia**, MS, PhD, D.CEP (Diplomate, Comprehensive Energy Psychology), President, Association of Comprehensive Energy Psychology

"An inspiring and comprehensive vision of the role of Healing Touch both for personal well-being and in the expanding role of energy healing in integrative health care."

> —**Barbara Stone**, PhD, LISW, D.CEP, Author of *Invisible Roots: How healing past life trauma can liberate your present*

"Dorothea has put together the m   ative book available to date about the first tw   '). It is a fascinating read for all interested i   study

D1534259

of spirituality and health. After a foreword by distinguished professor Jean Watson, Dorothea presents an amazing portrait of HT, divided into four sections and fifteen chapters. All that is followed by an excellent bibliography and appendices and a useful index.

"We would all be well-served if other complementary and alternative modalities would provide equally well-developed coverage of their experiences during the beginnings of the twenty-first century."
—**Bob Nunley**, Ph.D., Professor and Dean of Faculty, Holos University

"This special collection brings together the latest in developments of the Healing Touch Program, worldwide leaders in energy medicine. The text is a comprehensive overview of theory and practice of energy medicine and Healing Touch written by a collection of author experts in the field, including practical applications in a user-friendly guide for multiple audiences. What I have been teaching, researching and writing about for thirty plus years is what HT practitioners put into practice every day."
—**Jean Watson**, PhD, RN, AHN-BC, FAAN, Distinguished Professor of Nursing and Murchinson-Scoville Endowed Chair in Caring Science, University of Colorado Denver, Founder Watson Caring Science Institute www.watsoncaringscience.org

"Dr. Hover-Kramer's *Healing Touch Guidebook* celebrates the twentieth anniversary of this effective, non-invasive, and holistic healing art has flowered into a powerful force in the healthcare arena. This book provides a thorough overview of the many branches of the growing Healing Touch tree, including its foundation in the ethics of caring and its scientific roots. She reviews the many HT applications and celebrates the manner in which HT is being used to address problems occurring across the life span and adapted by practitioners across the planet. The Healing Touch movement has also inspired other energy-based healing practices, such as energy psychology. Like HT, energy psychology works with the human energetic matrix. Together HT and energy psychology offer new and realistic hope for change and transformation... from debilitating trauma to living normal lives again.

"In this book, Dr. Hover-Kramer rightly emphasizes the central role of practitioner self-care. Certainly, after twenty years of transforming people's lives and hearts, HT has earned the right to be included in any serious discussion about the future of healthcare. Congratulations to the Healing Touch Program community for reaching this milestone!"
—**Larry Stoler**, PhD, D.CEP, Psychologist, WholeHealth Chicago, Past President, The Association for Comprehensive Energy Psychology, Certified LifeForce Tao of Medical Qigong practitioner

"The new 2009 *Healing Touch Guidebook* by Dorothea Hover-Kramer provides a concise, easy-to-read, but comprehensive review of the history, background, science, methodology, healthcare application and future of Healing Touch. The complexity of this task, all delivered within parameters for easy access for the reader, would appear to be daunting, but in fact the material is delivered in such an accessible fashion that one comes away from the book feeling that they really know the subject. I've lectured at the Healing Touch Program's organization's annual meeting, written an article for their online magazine and experienced the technique from a number of practitioners. Now, however, I feel that I really have a grasp of all the nuances of this wonderful therapeutic technique."

—**Robert Scaer**, MD, Author of *The Body Bears the Burden: Trauma, dissociation and disease*, and *The Trauma Spectrum: Hidden wounds and human resiliency*

"The *Healing Touch Guidebook* is an extraordinary resource for healers, healthcare professionals and anyone interested in gaining a better understanding of the dynamics involved in Healing Touch. This book is a must-read for those interested in the research, conceptual underpinnings, and practical application of Healing Touch. It is certain to become one of the seminal, foundational books that address subtle, energy healing."

—**Lucia Thornton**, RN, MSN, AHN-BC Past-President American Holistic Nurses Association

"This book is the definitive guide to the Healing Touch Program (HTP). It will soon become the standard text for the first accredited modality in the field of Energy Medicine (EM) -- a key component of the new specialty of Integrative Holistic Medicine (IHM). Dorothea, an extraordinary energy healer herself, has woven together a beautiful tapestry of science, technique, application, and ethics, along with the expertise of HTP and EM pioneers, and infused it with the inspired vision of HTP founder, Janet Mentgen. It is both a practical and comprehensive guide to healing with love, as well as a wonderful gift for healthcare practitioners including anyone interested in self-care."

—**Rob Ivker**, DO, ABIHM, HTCP, Co-founder and Past-President, American Board of Integrative Holistic Medicine; Past-President, American Holistic Medical Association; Former Assistant Clinical Professor, University of CO School of Medicine; Author of best-selling, *Sinus Survival*.

Healing Touch Guidebook: Practicing the Art and Science of Human Caring

Twentieth Anniversary Edition

by Dorothea Hover-Kramer, EdD, RN, DCEP

Healing Touch Guidebook:
Practicing the Art and Science of Human Caring

Published by Healing Touch Program
20822 Cactus Loop, San Antonio, TX 78258

Author - Dorothea Hover-Kramer, EdD, RN, DCEP

ISBN 978-0-9790477-8-7

For individual orders and for information on special discount quantity orders please contact:

Healing Touch Program
(210) 497-5529 / FAX (210) 497-8532
info@HealingTouchProgram.com
www.HealingTouchProgram.com

Graphic Design - Billy Courtney, Matt Courtney, Margaret Nies
Typesetting – Margaret Nies
Cover Design - Billy Courtney
Cover Photo - Ginny Altmeyer
Printed in United States of America using soy based ink
First Edition, Second Printing - November 2010

To all those who seek new ways of healing.

Contents

SECTION I
THE FRAMEWORK FOR UNDERSTANDING
THE PRACTICE OF HEALING TOUCH

SECTION II
DESCRIPTION OF HEALING TOUCH
PRACTICES AND COURSEWORK

SECTION IV
ONGOING DEVELOPMENT OF THE
HEALING TOUCH PRACTITIONER

Greetings from the Healing Touch Program Director

Welcome to this anniversary edition celebrating twenty years of the Healing Touch Program! Whether you are a newcomer to Healing Touch (HT), a curious reader, or part of the worldwide HT community, I am delighted to welcome you to a book that I feel will serve as an ambassador for this natural, well-established, and effective form of energy medicine. The teachings of HT are so universal and cross cultural that they have been taught in thirty-two countries and are becoming more and more established in mainstream healthcare.

On a personal note, I can say that Healing Touch has changed my life in many ways since my first class in 1992 after I had already been a practitioner of Therapeutic Touch for ten years. Every aspect of me in my body / mind / spirit has been influenced in a positive way, stretching me to be most fully myself. While I was already oriented to scientific and spiritual awareness as a doctorally-prepared mental health nurse with in-depth study of healing and world religions, Healing Touch brought my soul forces of thinking and feeling into harmony with my will and intention. My thinking, feeling and willing came together in a way that not only created new ways of practicing holistic nursing, but a fresh perspective for integrating holistic and practical concepts into my everyday life. Students and practitioners from all over the world have expressed similar sentiments during my fifteen years of teaching

Healing Touch and in my role as Program Director since 2005.

I was honored to spend several days a week with Janet Mentgen, our founder, in the last few years of her life as she mentored me for the position of Program Director after I served as the first director of HT research starting in 1994. Janet did not like bringing attention to herself, but she answered the call to teach a new practice of energy healing. Over the years, she helped many nurses and allied healthcare personnel to remember their ability to foster healing in others by the focused use of caring intention. Despite many challenges and trials, Janet ensured that this form of energy therapy would be accepted in mainstream healthcare, in churches, in schools and institutions of higher learning and in home settings. Her vision was to see energy healing principles practiced in all possible environments. The Healing Touch Program (HTP) is dedicated to help manifest this vision.

With the leadership of Janet's resourceful daughter, Lisa Mentgen Gordon, HTP executive administrator, and the many thousand practitioners of the HT community, the Healing Touch Program is proud to carry on Janet's legacy to bring the worldwide standard curriculum developed with her colleagues to all corners of the world. If you feel inspired by this book, please join in spreading the light of Healing Touch in your community and share your thoughts, hopes and visions with us!

With joy and gratitude,

Cynthia Hutchison DNSc, RN, MSN, HTCP/I, Program Director

Give your hands to serve and your heart to love.
- Mother Theresa

Foreword

Jean Watson, PhD, RN, AHN-bc, FAAN

This new *Healing Touch Guidebook*, celebrating the twentieth anniversary of the Healing Touch Program's (HTP) origin and evolution, brings together the most contemporary and futuristic consciousness, scholarship and practices of Healing Touch worldwide. Dorothea Hover-Kramer, the author of six other books about energy therapies, and someone who has helped to establish this field, is the perfect author/coordinator/editor of this sophisticated guide to understanding the practice of Healing Touch. Cynthia Hutchison, HTP's Program Director and Lisa Mentgen Gordon, HTP's executive administrator, have successfully continued Janet Mentgen's legacy by maintaining and enhancing the only standardized energy medicine program that offers professional certification internationally.

This work pulls together comprehensive sources and levels of scholarship, scientific foundation, ethics, professional organization, application, expanded roles, and functions of Healing Touch around the globe. This work touches the heart and soul of Healing Touch, its origin and ongoing role related to Healing Touch as a spiritual–scientific-holistic-integrative practice for self, others, and society as a whole.

Hover-Kramer has incorporated key leaders in Healing Touch and energy medicine to ground this work in practice, application, and implementation. This range of contributors incorporates not only the research underpinning HT but offers exemplars of concrete practices among nurses, counselors, parents and others demonstrating its timeless and transcendent nature across situations, settings, and circumstances. It integrates lay and trans-disciplinary professional and practice fields, thus affirming how this practice applies to anyone who wishes to become skilled in this healing hands-on modality.

The intellectual–historical foundation of HT is based upon the most conventional current developments in Caring Science, Energy Medicine, MindBodySpirit Medicine, Consciousness Research, Heart Sciences, and other movements toward Caring-Healing models and methods for society and healthcare. This work reminds us that HT is one model for helping to transform the current techno-cure medically dominated system of materialistic medicine. As Ken Wilber has implied, the changes toward an integral model of thinking is beyond paradigms, but is related to the nature of the consciousness of the practitioner and the evolution of human consciousness.

Underlying the HT baseline is an increasing awareness that the highest level of consciousness is LOVE; and an acknowledgement that the greatest source of all Healing is LOVE. Thus, the basis of HT ultimately is drawing upon the infinite field of universal LOVE to re-pattern and realign self and other to be in 'right relation' with Source, Spirit. This approach helps all to understand that ultimately HT is working with the intelligence of the Human-Divine energy flow. This in turn becomes a critical caring-healing/wholeness modality for self and others regardless of situation, setting, and location in the world. It is a universal human-holy-spirit phenomenon of working with sacred energy of life-force, the mystery, the unknown, reconnecting with infinite Source. As Nightingale reminded: Healing Touch is helping to put the patient in best condition whereby nature can heal.

Other unique features of this work are the HTP teachings for addressing specific issues, such as pain relief, anxiety, and other conditions. The energy medicine model, the ten-step HT sequence, the explicit understandings of the chakra system, and specific energetic connections for health-illness conditions make this book a special asset and user-friendly blueprint for HT work.

Finally, this book brings together experts from the field, historic and contemporary scholars, leaders, and practitioners in education, curriculum, teaching, and diverse practices worldwide. It serves as a treatise and classic guide to Healing Touch in healthcare today and into the future.

Jean Watson, September 2009

Boulder, Colorado

Dr. Jean Watson is Distinguished Professor of Nursing and holds an endowed Chair in Caring Science at the University of Colorado Denver and Anschutz Medical Center Campus. She is founder of the original Center for Human Caring in Colorado and is a Fellow of the American Academy of Nursing. She previously served as Dean of Nursing at the University Health Sciences Center and is a Past President of the National League for Nursing. Her latest activities include Founder and Director of a new non-profit foundation: Watson Caring Science Institute. www.watsoncaringscience.org

As author /co-author of over 14 books on caring, Dr. Watson's latest books range from empirical measurements of caring, to new postmodern philosophies of caring and healing. Her books have received AJN books of the year awards and seek to bridge paradigms as well as point toward transformative models for the 21st century. A new revised edition of her first book, *Nursing: The Philosophy and Science of Caring* is now available (www.upcolorado.com). A new edition of *Assessing and Measuring Caring* was published in September, 2008 (Springer Publication, NY).

Author's Acknowledgements

Many people have contributed to the development and implementation of the international Healing Touch Program, many more than we can possibly mention. However, it is essential to acknowledge my primary ally for this book project, **Cynthia Hutchison**, the indefatigable Healing Touch Program Director. Without Cynthia's flow of discussions and weekly meditations over the months of writing, this book could not have happened. Every page was reviewed and approved by her for accuracy and to convey her dedicated enthusiasm for the ongoing work of HT.

It goes without saying that the Healing Touch Program gives ongoing immense appreciation to its founder **Janet Mentgen** for her healing vision and unceasing willingness to "do the work" as she called HT. She had an uncanny ability to capture the hearts of nurses and allied healthcare professionals and engage their interest with her hands-on methods and classes. The fact that HT was able to continue and grow as a viable worldwide force for healing after her transition in 2005 is a tribute to her organization which was led by her many colleagues, coworkers, Cynthia, and family members.

I also wish to thank **Lisa Mentgen Gordon**, HTP executive administrator, for serving as publisher of this book and her willing helpfulness at every turn. **Bill Mentgen** helped with copyrights and **Margaret Nies** effectively handled chapter illustrations and layout. **Stephanie Marohn** was the copy editor while **Billy Courtney** did the graphics and the cover design and **Ginny Altmeyer** provided the cover photo.

The contributing authors are mentioned separately on the next pages. They provided unique perspectives and enhanced the overall composition of the book.

Significant appreciation definitely must go to the lively community of HT practitioners who generously supported the program since its inception more than twenty years ago. Many of them, as readers will learn in this volume, are still active and exploring new aspects and applications of HT.

Here is a list (in alphabetical order) of the many practitioners who contributed stories, examples, summaries of their specialties and personal sharings. They enriched the book and made putting it together a great adventure for me.

Toni Adsit-Wilson	Kathryn Koches
Linda M. Aimone	Carol Komitor
Kathy Allen	Mary Lemons
Bill Badinger	Debbie Lundgren
Wanda Barboza	Susan MacIntosh
Dianne Bautch	Janna Moll
Tama Bevin	Jeannette Nienabar
Deanna Bogart	Katie Oberlin
Wanda Buckner	Lynne O'Donnell
Donna Chicoine	Peg Olson
Carol Crihfield	Wietzke van Oone
Becky Dailey	Lauri Pointer
Christina Devoe	Al Restoule
Roseann Geiser	Sharon Robbins
Sr. Catherine Louise Ginther	Connie Silva
Neil Gilbert	Kathy Sinnett
Kimberly Gray	Vicki Slater
Linda Griffeth	Linda Smith
Krista Hall	Patricia Springer
Linda Hallett	Barbara Starke
Nancy Kalfallah	Judy Stoddard
Nicole Kasemir	Beth Wright
Janis Kleinberger	Joyce Wong
Donna Kline	Teresa Wong
Rita Kluny	

I apologize for any incorrect spellings and hope I did not leave anyone out. I had no idea there would be such a strong response, and unfortunately could not include every story or detail. I have encouraged the leadership at HTP to consider doing a book of the many powerful healing stories I received and am keeping the file on hand, ready for future sharing.

My sincere good wishes extend to all within the Healing Touch Program community and the many who helped this book to become a reality!

---Dorothea Hover-Kramer

Contributing Authors

Cynthia Hutchison, DNSc., RN, HTCP/I, is the Program Director of the Healing Touch Program and was mentored in this position by Janet Mentgen, founder. A long time holistic nurse with a doctoral degree from Catholic University of America, she initiated the HT Research Program in 1994 and has maintained a private practice in Healing Touch since 1993. Teaching and administrating Healing Touch worldwide is one of Cynthia's greatest joys in life.

Sr. Rita Jean DuBrey, MSN, RN, HTCP/I, Sister of St. Joseph of Carondelet, is Director of the Center for Complementary Therapies at St. Mary's Hospital, Amsterdam, NY. She is a Clinical Nurse Specialist, a Credentialed Alcoholism and Substance Abuse Counselor, an accreditied T'ai Chi Chih Teacher and has been involved in the ministry of promoting wellness for over 25 years. She is a charter member of Healing Touch Professional Association and maintains an active Healing Touch community-based practice at St. Mary's Hospital, Amsterdam, NY.

Kathy Moreland Layte, RN, MScN, CS, HTCP/I, has been involved in HT since 1994 and chairs HTP's Research Advisory Council. A registered nurse for twenty-seven years, she served in a variety of roles in Canada and the United States in oncology and palliative care and was the first person in Canada to do HT research as part of her Master's thesis. Currently, she is a professor of nursing in the McMaster/Mohawk/Conestoga Nursing Program and is pursuing her PhD with a dissertation that explores the effect of HT on pain in the elderly.

James L. Oschman, Ph.D. is a cell biologist and biophysicist who is now a full-time author and presenter. In 1996 he wrote a series of 6 articles for the Journal of Bodywork and Movement Therapies; he then authored the book *Energy Medicine: the scientific basis* in 2000 which received wide circulation and a second book entitled *Energy Medicine in Therapeutics and Human Performance* was published in 2003. Lectures and workshops have taken him to dozens of countries throughout Europe and Asia, to South America, and to cities throughout the USA. www.energyresearch.us.

Sharon Scandrett-Hibdon Ph.D., RN, CFNP, HTCP/I, is a Family Nurse Practitioner in Family Medicine and a Clinical Specialist in Psychiatric Mental Health Nursing. She is a past president of the AHNA and founding elder of HT. Sharon is the current chair of Healing Touch Certification. She also is a certified instructor for the NARHA (North American Riding Handicap Association) and owns her own riding school in Iowa.

Author's Preface

The Naming of Healing Touch

Few may recall the details of how Healing Touch and the world-wide Healing Touch Program were named. I know because I was there. I was privileged to be present on May 1, 1989, when Janet Mentgen, Susan Morales, and I met to discuss ways the energy healing program that Janet was teaching in Colorado could become a national program for nurses and healthcare professionals.

As education chair of the American Holistic Nurses Association (AHNA) at that time and member of its leadership council for nine years, I saw the potential for expanding Janet's work to reach much wider audiences in professional healthcare settings. Janet Mentgen was already known to AHNA as the recipient of the Holistic Nurse of the Year award in 1988 for her untiring, successful efforts to promote understanding about energy healing in nursing.

I had seen Janet in action at a regional AHNA conference earlier that year in Florida. One of the seventy participants was an elderly lady with a chronic chest condition. She coughed all night long and kept her suitemates at the resort from getting their sleep. When Janet offered to conduct a healing session on someone the next day in a workshop, all of the suitemates pointed to that individual. Only too willing to be helped, she stepped forward. Janet assisted her in getting onto the treatment table while she continued to cough. Then Janet set her intention during a brief but notable moment and quickly brought her hands into the woman's energy field. Even though I did not understand

Janet's hand movements, it looked like an energetic ballet to me. I could see streamers of light coming off Janet's fingers while she pulled out what appeared to be dark fuzzy material from the lady's chest. I was fascinated with Janet's spinning hand movements, which added power to her concentration while the energy flowed like showers of light from her hands. I later came to understand this method as a form of *chelation* similar to the methods used by physicians to cleanse the blood of toxins--only this was an energetic, nonmaterial version of the process.

After the session, the lady smiled and got off the table. The treatment lasted about forty minutes during which time she never coughed. She suffered no further coughing paroxysms and everyone slept well that night.

Years later a friend who knew this woman told me that the woman remained free of coughing spells for the rest of her life and the chronic chest condition never recurred. She died from a stroke fifteen years after Janet's healing demonstration.

The remarkable healing that I witnessed left a deep impression on me. I asked Janet about her course and how I could come to understand what we had experienced. Janet described her coursework to me and I started putting ideas together. It occurred to me that developing an educational program which could reach nurses and allied healthcare professionals across the country was entirely feasible. The curriculum that Janet had taught for several years at Red Rocks Community College, CO could be redesigned to be given on weekends in the format of five workshops across the nation. With this intention, Janet and I planned to meet to design such a traveling curriculum.

Susan Morales joined our meeting as an already skilled Therapeutic Touch practitioner with a strong interest in the many additional techniques evident in Janet's program. I was attending one of Dr. Jean Watson's conferences in Denver early in May of 1989, so the three of us met at Janet's home to practice energy healing and talk about the teaching program we wanted to design.

After our beginning meditation, we stopped to think about a name for this program. I felt that calling Janet's teachings Therapeutic Touch did not do justice to the many unique aspects and methods of her program. By then, Therapeutic Touch was already well established as a nursing modality with a specific training curriculum. Although it might have been tempting to use the same name for increased visibility, ethical concerns told us we needed a new name. We recognized that Janet's work incorporated teachings from many other healers, many of whom were scientifically oriented, and that it included numerous chakra and biofield interventions. We mused together "This is healing work...it has energetic components...it is similar to Therapeutic Touch but different... it embodies caring..." We passed these thoughts around a few times and, with the grace of the moment, one of us said, "How about Healing Touch?" There was a stunned period of silence, and then agreement: "Yes, that's a good name. Let's do it!"

And so we proceeded. We discussed how Janet's material might be taught in weekend intensives and qualify for continuing education credits for nurses. The networks of the American Holistic Nurses Association could help us launch the program in its six national regions with Janet leading and assisted by some of the most eager followers. The material fell into five separate levels that could be given in weekend modules rather than within a college semester. Since I had been involved in continuing education for many years, writing behavioral objectives, course outlines, and evaluation criteria for each weekend module came easily. As soon as the first course was ready for continuing education credits, we planned the schedule. In the latter half of 1989, Janet's new business, Colorado Center for Healing Touch (now renamed the Healing Touch Program), offered two courses, one at the University of Tennessee in Memphis with Sharon Scandrett-Hibdon coordinating, and one in Gainesville, Florida, with me as Janet's assistant.

The HT Program is Born

The rest is history, as the saying goes. Our first single-sheet handouts grew into instruction manuals as we went along. By 1990, Janet taught twenty-five classes across the United States and Canada with various helpers. Today the program calendar has grown to more than seven hundred annual offerings and Healing Touch is actively taught in more than thirty-two countries! From the beginning, the work resonated with healthcare professionals across the United States. The first countries after the United States to embrace Healing Touch were Canada, Australia, and New Zealand. In 1992, Mary Jo Bulbrook teamed up with Janet to produce the first attractive computer-generated course manuals.

After a long illness, Janet Mentgen passed away on September 15, 2005, three days after making her final public appearance before more than six hundred Healing Touch practitioners at the annual international HT conference. The Healing Touch Program has grown since then, with further development and professionalizing of the curricular notebooks for all five levels of the course, the instructor training manual, and other supportive courses including Advanced Practice classes, self-care classes, a children's program, case study books, and a monthly complimentary on-line magazine. Many other offerings and services, including the annual HTP worldwide conferences, reach thousands of interested professionals and clients.

My previous textbooks explaining Janet's methods, the philosophy of HT, and its relevance to healing were released in 1996 and 2002. Published by Delmar International, they continue to enjoy wide circulation.

In 1993, a core group of nursing educators that included me developed a certification program from the materials originally given by Janet and refined within the continuing education format. I strongly supported the idea of certification for a number of reasons. The academic recognition we had achieved through our continuing education courses was gaining momentum and growing numbers of practitioners had completed all five levels of the program including its mentorship component. Such skilled practitioners from all healthcare fields needed a valid credential. Today, practitioners certified after studying the original curriculum through the Healing Touch Program (HTP) number more than three thousand worldwide.

By 1996, AHNA had recognized and encouraged many other continuing education programs in addition to Healing Touch. They had also developed their own credential for Holistic Nursing Certification. The time seemed ripe to let all of these programs function independently while AHNA maintained its well-earned status as the nation's "umbrella" holistic nursing organization. In the same year, HT certification administration was transferred from AHNA to a new autonomous certifying organization Janet created especially for Healing Touch.

HTP was expanded and enriched by the many contributions of its generous practitioners. Many new developments and applications to all aspects of the human life cycle followed. Thousands of healthcare professionals' lives have been touched by HTP. Hundreds of thousands of people have benefited from receiving Healing Touch in times of physical, emotional, and spiritual need.

From Dream to Reality

This book is the newest and most complete text about HT and is part of the celebration of the twenty-year anniversary since the founding of HT in 1989. Despite the phenomenal growth in diversity of HT in personal and professional applications, the standard curriculum of the Healing Touch Program remains consistent with the intention and vision of the original collegial group who participated with Janet Mentgen in cocreating this beautiful, professional, and effective program of hands-on healing.

It has been my delight to see this program develop. Although I have moved further into my practice as a psychotherapist and a contributor to advancing energy psychotherapy in the past decade, the principles of HT continue to resonate within my work and serve as a foundation in my practice. When I cofounded the Association for Comprehensive Energy Psychology (ACEP) in 1999, I insisted the Association must encompass not only those caregivers who focus on the meridians and their acupoints to bring emotional relief, but also include the many practitioners who work with the human energy field and the energy centers as seen in HT practice.

Early in 2009, Cynthia Hutchison, program director of the Healing Touch Program, and Lisa Mentgen Gordon, executive administrator of HTP, approached me about writing this new book about Healing Touch. I couldn't resist. Despite my overly full schedule, my inner advisor unequivocally said, "Yes!"

At a dinner meeting to discuss plans for the book, Cynthia and I enjoyed Chinese food. Of course, we checked our fortune cookies for advice. Mine read: "You will be invited to participate in a team project. Be sure to collaborate." I took it as a direct confirmation of my participation in the book project!

As often occurs, an incubating dream brought me a worthy metaphor. I dreamt I was hosting a great banquet. Healing Touch practitioners akin to the ones I had met in my recent presentations started arriving at my home and each brought exquisitely crafted foods. I remember the colors and the smells of each food item as it was given to me, and I carefully arranged the dishes on a large table. I thanked and hugged each contributor for the incredible feast we were going to share. Then we together thanked the Creator for the bounty placed before us and for the joy of being together again, before digging in and partying.

As the book project began to take shape, I realized how each contribution was indeed a wonderful, separate dish while at the same time part of a much larger banquet. Stories and vignettes started arriving via the Internet, fax, and mail. I unwrapped each one with gratitude and placed it in its portion of the grand banquet: the book and its chapters. The banquet is now ready to be shared with guests and readers from all parts of the world and all paths of life.

As newcomers will learn, HT comes from the heart and soul of all who want to help others. It is a gift that expands the more it is given. I invite you to explore with me in the adventure of learning about the underlying principles as well as the many new developments in Healing Touch!

Dorothea Hover-Kramer, September 1, 2009

Port Angeles, WA

About This Book

This book may be an opening, a beginning, for interested readers from all walks of life. It is intended to help expand and deepen understanding of the healing process in both newcomers and seasoned practitioners. No matter where you are in your own journey of discovery, this work is an invitation to widen your exploration of the many facets of HT and its conceptual framework with focus on theory, science, research, and actual practice.

The book is organized into four sections. The first section presents the essential background material, science, and research about energy therapies such as Healing Touch; the second part gives a summary of the major methods and concepts currently taught within the Healing Touch Program core curriculum in Levels One through Five; the third part demonstrates some of the many applications, both personal and professional, for Healing Touch concepts as they are currently practiced worldwide; and the final portion focuses on the ongoing personal and spiritual development of HT practitioners.

Practitioners of energy-oriented therapies such as Healing Touch come from many social service professions. Many HT certified practitioners are nurses because of the base of HT in the art and science of holistic nursing. In addition, they include massage and somatic therapists, social workers, physical and occupational therapists, physicians, psychologists, counselors, teachers, chaplains, and other allied healthcare professionals. They also include rapidly growing numbers of dedicated laypersons, many of whom have completed the certification program. HT practitioner are visible in both mainstream healthcare and private settings around the globe.

Throughout the book, the word "practitioner" is used to describe the person who sets clear intention to give focused care to the recipient. Synonyms used for this term include "healer," "facilitator," and "caregiver." The recipient of this care is most often called "client" or "patient," depending on their entry point in healthcare settings.

Both women and men serve as practitioners and seek assistance as clients, so gender-specific terms ("he" or "she") are used interchangeably. Names given to clients in the true stories cited are fictional to protect confidentiality. I gratefully acknowledge the participation of the international community of HT practitioners who shared their stories for this book.

Section I

The Framework for Understanding the Practice of Healing Touch

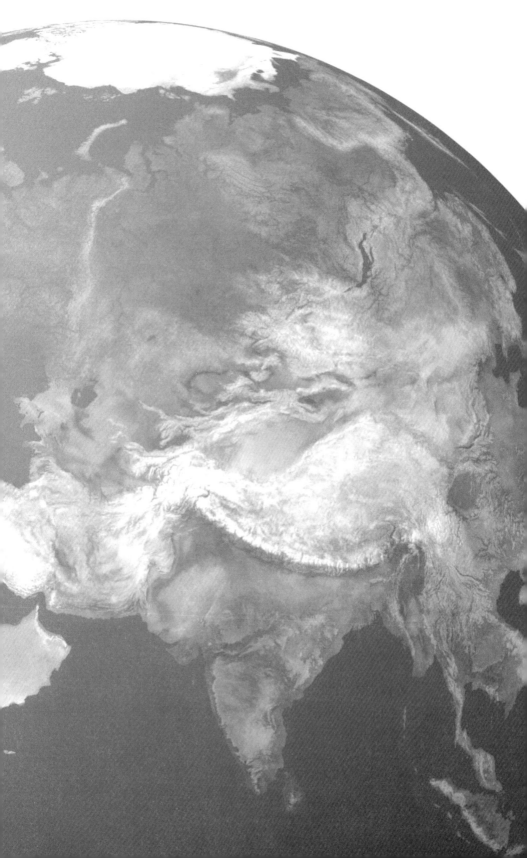

Chapter 1

The Worldwide Impact of Healing Touch in Healthcare Settings

Though your destination is not yet clear
You can trust the promise of this opening;
Unfurl yourself into the grace of a beginning
That is at one with your life's desire.

—John O'Donohue

Welcome to the fascinating world of Healing Touch! This dynamic and evolving program has reached and influenced hundreds of thousands of people in need over the past twenty years. A grateful and growing community of clients and patients has experienced one or more opportunities for pain relief, deepening relaxation, increased sense of well-being, and relief from anxiety and stress through Healing Touch (HT). More profoundly, caregivers utilizing HT (including the several thousand certified practitioners) have learned methods for trusting their intuitive knowing and are providing a meaningful shift in understandings of human caring.

HT Founder Janet Mentgen believed in starting any new course by giving workshop participants a direct experience of HT before delving into its underlying principles and teaching specific methods. For the novice who seeks an idea of the whole picture before learning its components, we'll begin this book with an overview of HT practice with real-life examples. For seasoned practitioners, the five examples given here may jog memories or help you recognize the many times and places you have seen HT in action.

Examples of Healing Touch in Practice

Carol, a nurse on a medical-surgical floor of a community hospital, is giving pain medication to the patient in room 102. "Pills, pills, pills," he complains, and then sighs, "Don't you have anything else you can do for me?"

Carol explains she has learned techniques from a program called Healing Touch (HT), which might help to make the medication more effective and provide some relaxation. There are no known side effects with HT. The brief explanation puts her patient at ease and he gladly accepts her invitation.

Carol centers herself and carefully moves her hands over her patient from head to toe several times to release congestion in his energy field and then holds her hands still above the most painful area of his body. Within a few minutes, he is resting more comfortably as his eyes close. Carol quietly tells him she is leaving and puts a "Do Not Disturb" sign at the door so her patient can get helpful rest.

****

Sondra is a hospice social worker who has learned HT. Her home visits to severely ill patients, many of them in terminal stages of illness, are emotionally challenging to her. She carefully centers herself before each home visit to release her fears and expectations in order to make sure she can be fully present for the families she visits.

This day Sondra is visiting a family who just admitted their mother/grandmother to hospice care. Dina is an elderly patient dying of lung cancer. Sondra gathers the data required to develop the hospice plan of care with family members. Before leaving, she wants to give the family some additional resources to help overcome their feelings of helplessness in being caregivers at the end of life. She explains briefly that HT may be helpful to their loved one and administers, with Dina's permission, Magnetic Passes and the Chakra Spread (both are described in chapter 6).

Dina clearly relaxes during the twenty-minute treatment as the family watches intently. Afterward, interested family members comment and Sondra allows time to discuss and review the methods so that the family can do them with Dina in between hospice visits. Dina's daughter expresses her gratitude: "We've wondered what we could do to help. Thank you for showing us something we can do." They feel empowered to help in a new and effective way.

****

Timmy is a restless five-year-old who has had a very busy day in kindergarten, a birthday party, a big bump on his knee from a fall, and a long soccer game. At bedtime, he is still totally wound up and the idea of going to sleep has no place in his busy mind.

Timmy's mother learned HT first aid in a parenting workshop at her community center. She decides to try out several of the approaches she learned. She starts by reading him a very boring story and gently touching each of his restless limbs. Then she makes long, caring sweeps above his body while singing a lullaby. Within a few minutes, Timmy is sound asleep.

****

John is a counselor with many years of experience in treating adults and children. Recently, he added energy therapy methods including HT to his other psychotherapeutic skills.

While on an airplane trip, John hears screams of pain from a nine-month-old baby who is on the lap of a parent a few rows away. John visits the parents when the seatbelt sign goes off. He introduces himself and explains his background, including information about ways to relieve the pain of ear canal congestion by helping the child's energy system release the blockage that causes pain. Anxiety and fears can also be relieved very quickly at the hands of trained practitioners. He gives them website contact information so they can find out more about HT.

Although the parents seem a bit skeptical and refuse his offer at first, the thought of relief from the constant crying causes them to change their minds. With their informed consent in place, John sits next to the mother who is holding her son and, after centering himself, brings his hands into the child's energy field.

Mother, child, and John make eye contact while John tells a story of someone in a similar situation. The child stops a moment and starts to listen. John explains he is going to move his hands around the ears to help relieve congestion. He moves his hands above the ears for a few minutes and seemingly brushes away the pressure, then holds his hands still over the child's ears without physical touch to help rebalance the energy. The child looks around as if surprised about the quiet and then starts making happy sounds while looking at the toy his mother has pulled out. He snuggles with her and becomes progressively more relaxed.

The relief on the crowded airplane is palpable.

****

Jerry is an advanced registered nurse practitioner working in an intensive care unit. He has gained the respect of physicians and other staff by having a firm grasp of the methods essential for running the ICU and keeping himself calm in a crisis.

Although he does not speak a great deal about his certification as a Healing Touch practitioner, the staff is aware of what they call his "magic hands." During a shift at the ICU, one of the other nurses reports that her patient has suffered a sudden onset of prolonged atrial fibrillation. When the crash cart and related personnel arrive, they do everything they can for the patient but with little effect. Finally, the physician in charge says, "Jerry, it's time for your magic hands either to help this person come back or to pass on."

Despite the hubbub, Jerry centers himself as he learned in HT classes and asks that the patient's highest good be served. He releases attachment to the outcome of his intervention. He holds his hands still above the patient's chest area while affirming his intention to be a facilitator for the universal energy flow. Gradually, as the din of the crash cart and alarm lights recede, the patient begins to stir and finally speaks. "I think I had a close call," she comments. "Thank you for being with me. I guess it was not my time to go."

Jerry smiles and thanks the Source of unlimited energy that seems to have been present during the crisis. He leaves the patient breathing evenly as her heart rhythms vibrate in sync with each other again. He briefly acknowledges the peace of the healing that occurred and goes on to his next task in the ICU.

****

Stories like these are coming from all over the world about real-life experiences with the energy-oriented methods of Healing Touch. HT is taking a mainstream position in many hospitals, home care programs, hospices, and nursing homes as part of the new integrative medicine movement. It is also presented in many nontraditional settings such as schools and community centers. HT is becoming accepted as a complement to conventional medical treatment approaches. Healthcare professionals, laypersons, and the many recipients of HT have come to value its collaborative gifts of relieving physical and emotional distress.

Equally notable is the prevalence of HT practitioners who now come from many walks of life other than traditional nursing. Although in the early days of HT, nursing provided the primary focus for its development, the program is now reaching the caregivers from many disciplines including massage therapists, physical therapists, occupational therapists, chiropractors, physicians, psychotherapists, chaplains, and counselors. In addition, members of the public are learning HT procedures in parenting classes, disability support groups, hospice and hospital volunteer training, retirement centers, and spiritual study groups.

Healing Touch as a Needed Presence in the Fast Pace of Twenty-First Century Life

Healing Touch is best understood as a philosophy of healing, a sacred healing art, and a way to actualize the principles of human caring as advanced by Dr. Jean Watson. Although human caring is a core concept for nurses and healthcare professionals, the actual components of "care" are sometimes shrouded in conflicting expectations and meanings. Although the specifics of care may vary across cultures, caring is universal and timeless at the human level, transcending societies, religions, belief systems, and geographic boundaries. It involves extending from oneself to reach out to others and the community; it becomes a way of thinking that affects all of life. Caring is humanity's connector. As Dr. Watson puts it, "In this reminder of health-centered knowing and wisdom beyond words and conventional knowledge, our basic humanness transcends circumstance, time, and place. Our being and becoming more humane and evolved allows us to engage once again in compassionate human service and science, motivated by love, both human and Cosmic."[1]

As a program that actualizes caring principles, HT provides energy-based therapeutic approaches by utilizing a number of techniques to assess and treat the human energy system. The goal of HT interventions is to restore wholeness in the client via therapeutic connection to an intentional and heart-centered practitioner. The seemingly simple hands-on methods of HT exemplify the essence of human caring in deeply profound ways.

Healing is best understood as ongoing movement toward, health, harmony, and wholeness. This ongoing dynamic is multidimensional since we human beings are multifaceted in nature. For example, we have bodies that respond to the thoughts and attitudes generated from the mind and to the feelings generated by our emotions. Thus, healing often involves recognizing and releasing strong negative emotions or learning to change limiting beliefs patterns. Physical pain relief is only one component of healing because thoughts and feelings also impact the body. Ultimately, healing results in finding deeper connections with inner wisdom and can lead to a sense of spiritual transformation.

In today's busy world, opportunities for such genuine healing of body, emotions, mind, and spirit are a rarity. Although most of human history included emphasis on whole-person healing, conventional medical practice in the twentieth and twenty-first centuries has focused predominantly on removal of distressing physical symptoms via surgery, radiation, chemical interventions, or medications from a huge pharmacopeia of prescribed drugs and chemotherapies. This focus continues to advance development of high technology with ever-diminishing human contact or attention to the psychological and spiritual needs of the patient. Caregivers, whether professionals or laypersons, also suffer from emotional impoverishment because of the intense focus on high-tech procedures and emphasis on measurable outcomes for cost containment.

The word "healing" comes from the Greek term holos, which underlies the concept of wholeness as in "to make whole." Closely aligned is the word "holistic," which is currently used to describe the many approaches to healing of all aspects of a person. Thus, the holistic health concepts advanced in the last thirty years offer healing to human body, mind, and spirit—to restore wholeness in the entire person. Whole-person healing is actually a reiteration of traditional medical practices known for thousands of years in human history. Only in the last century has conventional medicine focused almost entirely on the more tightly defined idea of cure. Cure has come to mean that the perceived cause of a problem and its bothersome symptoms are removed. As seen in present-day Western medical care, curing provides a decidedly narrow focus in which other human factors are often marginalized, and a lack of cure, or death, is seen as defeat.

Many practitioners view HT as an answer to their desire to rekindle the fires of person-centered caring. Many practitioners call energy therapies the "missing link" in healthcare. In addition to validating humanistic service to others, the practice of HT also engenders a profound sense of the sacred, as we shall see further on.

The State of the Healing Touch Program on Its Twentieth Anniversary—2009

There is not room in this volume to give specific details about the vast expansion of HT since 1989, the year of its inception. Currently, offerings of the five-level practitioner certification training number more than 750 each year. (Description of the five-level course curriculum with its major content and methods is given in chapters 5–9). Once practitioners graduate from the standardized curriculum, they can choose to apply for international certification with the autonomous HT Certification Board.

In addition, numerous advanced practice courses and specialty courses are offered by the HT Program office to provide extended educational opportunities for students and practitioners (described in more detail in chapter 12). Given mostly in North America, the offerings of specialty courses number more than fifty each year.

Basic and advanced courses are taught all over the United States including Alaska and Hawaii. In addition, HT is taught in thirty-two other countries including Canada, Mexico, Peru, Australia, New Zealand, Japan, Germany, Italy, Switzerland, Finland, Denmark, the Netherlands, South Africa, Nepal, and India.

Current updates and course listings are sent out each month via HTP's outstanding Energy Magazine.[2] This monthly e-zine currently reaches over 12,000 subscribers with each publication and is growing.

At least 100,000 nurses and allied health caregivers have taken at least one level of HT training. Everyone who has taken the first level is encouraged to participate in one of the hundreds of local and regional HTP groups existing worldwide. Also active networks offer regional, national, and international conferences. HT practitioners are a significant force for influencing and changing the face of healthcare.

One additional valuable feature of the Healing Touch Program is its emphasis on personal development of the practitioner. This focus has been part of the program since its inception. No HT method can be utilized by an ethical practitioner or neophyte without the preparations of personal centering and grounding—releasing the burdens of the day, coming to a sense of inner calm, and setting intention on behalf of the person receiving the intervention. This ensures the integrity of the healer's energy field as well as provides essential protection against untoward effects from connecting with the client's often diminished or imbalanced energies. Over the years, this injunction against casual practice without adequate thought or inner preparation has brought great benefits to hundreds of thousands of clients. It has also enhanced the overall well-being of HT practitioners.

—ഝ—

The ongoing dynamic of Healing Touch as it has evolved over the past twenty years will be explored in the chapters to come. We'll also investigate the underlying concepts of energy therapies since they are becoming well-grounded in theory, science, and research. This book is a celebration of the twenty years of service that caring practitioners have brought and an invitation to learn for all interested newcomers!

Chapter Notes

1. J. Watson, *Nursing: The philosophy and science of caring* (Boulder, CO: University of Colorado Press, 2008), 240.

2. To receive the free e-zine or find out about current HT Program offerings: www.healingtouchprogram.com; e-mail: info@HealingTouch-program.com; telephone: 210-497-5529.

Chapter 2

History and Theories of Energy Healing

Sharon Scandrett-Hibdon, PhD, RN, HTCP/I, and
Dorothea Hover-Kramer, EdD, RN, DCEP

Though no one can go back and make a brand new start, anyone can start from now and make a brand new ending.
—Anonymous

Brief History of Energy Healing

Early humans undoubtedly recognized their own life energy which we define here as the vitality, the aliveness, or the force in all living things. The presence of energy, or vital life force, is most obvious when one notes the difference between life and death. Our ancestors found their vital life force could best be protected and preserved by living in harmony with their natural surroundings.

We know from oral traditions, for example, that Native Americans identified closely with nature and responded to the many forces in their world in an intuitive way. They saw wind, sun, stars, water, plants, and animals as having magical powers and specific meanings. As people more than thirty thousand years ago learned how to survive, they began to draw on nature's powers to assist them in dealing with injuries, in attracting game to their area, and in finding the right plants for food. Often this attunement to natural resources consisted of invoking the essence of a plant or animal to ask for guidance. Herbs, for example, were consulted to determine whether they could relieve certain maladies and bring healing. Evidence of the strong interrelationship between humans and the forces of nature can be seen in the shields, caves, and tepees the ancients painted with symbols of power objects—images of animals or nature signs like the wind, sun, or lightning.

Information was shared orally as people experimented and found success in using thoughts, symbols, and certain herbs. Some individuals were especially sensitive in communicating with nature's energies and began accumulating knowledge to help those in need. Survival, however, was the overriding focus in the brief lifetimes of our ancient ancestors.

As humans became oriented to agriculture about ten thousand years ago, they increased their understanding of planetary seasons to maximize the harvest. They came to know the healing properties of plants. This information was protected and passed down through generations of families to facilitate survival. Our ancestors also designated special environments filled with personal meaning for them as sacred places. Such sites included natural springs, unusual rock formations, and groves of awe-inspiring trees. Some of the most powerful knowledge became hidden and known only to a few people. Often, such hidden, occult knowledge ensured power over others. Those especially skilled in the use of healing powers were labeled shamans, healers, or medicine men. They were respected, sometimes feared, but always considered necessary to the tribe's survival. Women, the herb gatherers, had similar knowledge, but used it only when necessary to assist, for example, with childbirth. Healers felt responsible for the safety and health of their tribe. Early shamans utilized massage and magical rituals to restore what they considered to be the proper interrelationship between humans, nature, and the spirit world.[1]

Energy approaches to healing were used for thousands of years and have been documented worldwide. Huang Ti Ching Su Wen established their use in China 2500–5000 years ago.[2] The Egyptian third dynasty and healers of ancient Egypt freely used energy symbols like the *ankh* to enhance the breath of life and healing. [3] The land of the Wiracocha, now Bolivia and Peru, abounded in *huaca*, the spirit energies of sacred healing places.[4] Indian traditions called the vital life force *prana* and the Chinese word for such energy is *qi* (pronounced *chee*); both of these terms have been widely for more than five thousand years and are still in use today. The biofield, another name for the human energy field, was acknowledged by Hippocrates in classical Greece. In 500 BC, Pythagoras referred to the luminous body that could produce cures and Paracelsus called human energy *illiaster*.[5] In the Christian era, Jesus' ability to heal with his presence is often noted, and healers became part of religious traditions.[6] To this day, the ancient Christian church's word for energy, *spiritus*, is frequently used to represent higher aspects of human consciousness and forms the root of words such as "spirit" and "spiritual."

In the Middle Ages, common people used Christian healing and pagan folk medicine side by side. Medicinal interventions and healing practices were quite similar to each other and there was little differentiation between magical and herbal cures. Monks recorded medieval medical practices.[7] As belief in malevolent possession by spirits and daemons was prevalent, people dispelled their energies with charms, amulets, prayers, chanting, and herbs. Practitioners often sang into open wounds with special incantations to assist the patient's healing.[8]

As medicine became more of a science in the sixteenth century, alchemists and apothecaries developed treatments for the wealthy while most of the populace continued to seek out the local shaman or "wys" woman to effect cures. Family health was largely addressed by females while matters of the spirit were dominated by male shamans.[9] In its bid to establish and perpetuate power over the masses, the Christian church actively discouraged shamanic practices. Pagan practitioners, male and female, were labeled witches and severely persecuted or killed to stamp out their practices.

Today, energy modalities are regaining acceptance. Modern medicine is gradually acknowledging energy as a way of understanding interactions within human physiology.[10] New discoveries are opening doors and research is being done to verify the many new energy-based resources that assist in diagnosis and healing.[11] Present-day physicists are further scrutinizing and analyzing Einstein's understanding of subtle energies. He concluded that everything is energy and organized as energetic fields.[12]

Verifiable uses of energy fields in medicine include measurements of patient's varying electromagnetic vibrations via gamma rays, X rays, ultraviolet light, visible light, infrared, microwaves, radio waves, and sound waves. Subtle energies that influence and course through the human body are more difficult to verify, but current science is finding increasing means to measure them. Subtle energies include the human biofield and its energy centers, meridian pathways, basic grids, subtle thought fields, subtle electrical fields, and morphogenetic fields, which are presumed to transfer information between human generations.[13] Planetary energies such as earth's magnetosphere and solar emanations also have known direct influences on human life.

Principles of the Human Energy System

In Healing Touch, practice is primarily focused on the human energy field, also called the *biofield*, and the major human energy centers, the chakras. As mentioned, there are numerous other patterns in the human energy system that have been identified by sensitive healers and scientists. For our discussion here, we focus on the two energy components that are most central to Healing Touch.

It is helpful to learn to experience life energy consciously. As you begin to sense your own energy, you may sense your heartbeat, your breath, and your sense of inward peace. As you quiet yourself and pay attention, your sensitivity to minute changes and differences increases. Learning to do this through meditation connects you to your inner being and innate wisdom. A fun exercise is to explore different settings in order to sense the energies around you. Allow yourself to experience the following: sitting in a church, walking in a lovely forest, breathing deeply at the beach, listening by a stream, shopping in a mall, looking around in a bar, and standing in a hospital. Seeking out these encounters greatly sharpens your attunement to the different energies in your environment and within you.

As your sensitivity increases, it is helpful to focus on the varying energies of plants, animals, and people. Allow your whole being to be with the energy of another living presence. Animal energies are fascinating. You may receive impressions of thoughts or emotions, for the energetic field "speaks." In other words, each living biofield carries information. If you notice no perceptible energy from someone else's field, it may be that both fields (yours and the other person's) are vibrating at similar frequencies. Usually, differences in vibrational intensities make it easier to sense the energy of another person. Marked differences are often noted with individuals who are ill since their energy vibrations are often diminished or constricted. On the other hand, personal encounters with vibrant, effective speakers usually lift our own vibrational levels and we may notice excitement and increased personal vigor.

As energy medicine is relatively new in its language, learn to describe what you experience with your own terminology. The Healing Touch Program has collected vivid descriptions of energy perceptions from its many students and practitioners. These can be as varied as the practitioners themselves (see table 6.1 in chapter 6). Remember, everyone's perception is "correct" because the energy is filtering through each person's unique biofield. By way of analogy, consider the varied ways the same object will look when viewed through different-colored lenses.

Healthy human biofields have many variations as they can feel full, vibrant, wispy, thick, light, dense, or solid. Janet Mentgen, founder of Healing Touch, often said it was necessary to experience at least one hundred human biofields before one could understand what is "normal." Her wisdom encouraged students to keep an open mind and to learn by comparing and contrasting their experiences.

The human biofield, also known as the *aura*, is composed of multiple layers as depicted in figure 2.1. These layers are viewed by some intuitive healers as corresponding with the chakra system. More subtle layers extend outward, but the ones illustrated are the most perceptible and frequently used in HT interventions.

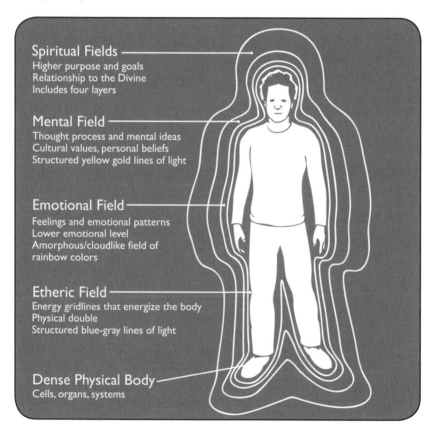

Spiritual Fields
Higher purpose and goals
Relationship to the Divine
Includes four layers

Mental Field
Thought process and mental ideas
Cultural values, personal beliefs
Structured yellow gold lines of light

Emotional Field
Feelings and emotional patterns
Lower emotional level
Amorphous/cloudlike field of
rainbow colors

Etheric Field
Energy gridlines that energize the body
Physical double
Structured blue-gray lines of light

Dense Physical Body
Cells, organs, systems

Figure 2.1. Human Biofield with Layers Evident.

The biofield is considered the container of personal energies. The personal field is full and expanded when we are happy and vital, or it can be contracted, pulling in closer to the physical body, when we experience sadness, depression, or health problems. The biofield emanates from the physical body and interacts with the environment, bringing in as well as sending out energy. Evidence of the perceived aura is seen in classical religious paintings as an emanation from the body, particularly the halo around the head. The field is known to contain information about the organism in a holographic way and can thus assist in bringing about healing.[14]

As one begins to work with the biofield or aura, it is helpful to develop sensitivity to its major layers or levels, which interpenetrate the physical body but may extend beyond the skin surface based on the person's current physical, emotional, mental or spiritual state. These include: the *etheric* layer or level , which usually extends out about two inches from the physical body; the *emotional* layer, generally at six to ten inches beyond the body; the *mental* or causal layer which is about twelve or more inches away; and the *astral*, the fourth energy body, which extends approximately two to three feet beyond the physical. The more subtle energy layers could extend even farther and include the *etheric template* (blueprint for the physical body), the celestial body, and the *ketheric template* (blueprint for the spiritual dimension of the person).[15]

Finding the outermost edge of the aura is helpful in determining the shape of the field around the physical body. As sensitivity develops, one can feel the edges of the encased layers more easily while remembering that each layer is enfolded with those closer to the body. All are connected to the center of the body and may overlap or interpenetrate each other. These layers or levels alternate between being structured and more fluid.[16] The interactive layers or levels may co-exist in the same space with different vibrational frequencies just as radio channels and sound waves can simultaneously occupy the same space. The more vitality someone has, the larger and more energetic the biofield will be. Since the personal field is a hologram, all aspects are affected by working with one part of the whole.

The biofield also contains major and minor energy centers which move energy throughout the field layers. Such energy centers are noted in many indigenous cultures, and the best-known term is *chakra*, the Sanskrit word for "spinning vortex."[17] There are seven major chakras from the base of the spine to the top of the head. In addition, there are minor energy vortices at every joint in the human body, including the tiny ones of the fingers, wrists, ankles, and toes.

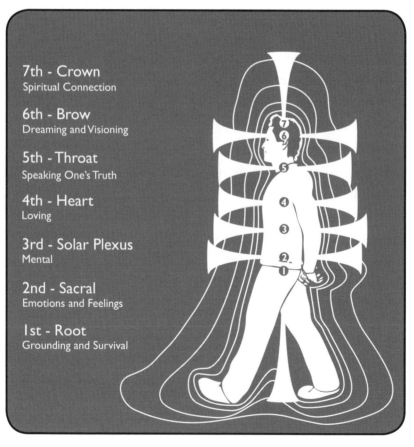

7th - Crown
Spiritual Connection

6th - Brow
Dreaming and Visioning

5th - Throat
Speaking One's Truth

4th - Heart
Loving

3rd - Solar Plexus
Mental

2nd - Sacral
Emotions and Feelings

1st - Root
Grounding and Survival

Figure 2.2. The Seven Major Chakras.

Memory is encoded in these energy transmitters. Each major chakra relates to essential body organs and endocrine glands in its proximity. Assessing the chakras gives practitioners information about the location of energy blockages in their clients. Psychological as well as physiological health is reflected in the state of each chakra as summarized in table 2.1. In addition, chakras are seen as "centers of consciousness" since they relate to the developmental stages of human personality and spirituality.

Chakra Name	Location	Physiological	Psychological Function
Root	Base of spine	Stress responses, survival mechanisms	Sense of safety, trust, will to live
Sacral	Below navel	Lower digestion, reproductive system	Feelings, desires, sexuality, ability to attract others and release unwanted attentions
Solar Plexus	Below the sternum	Upper digestion, pancreas, liver, and spleen	Clear thinking, self-esteem, healthy self-interest, effective assertiveness
Heart	Mid-chest	Heart rhythms, circulation, immune and lymphatic systems	Love, forgiveness, transformation, reaching out to others, altruism
Throat	Front and back of neck	Breath, vocal chords, speech, hearing	Self-expression, creativity, speaking one's truth
Brow	Mid-forehead	Lower brain functions, sight, smell	Compassion, insight, imagination, intuition, inspiration
Crown	Top of head	Upper brain functions, symbol-making, cognitive processes	Aligning with spirit, connecting with true nature and purpose and one's higher consciousness

Table 2.1. The chakras and their predominant physiological and psychological aspects

Human energy is constantly in motion. The biofield radiates, emanating and flowing with vital life force. Even our cells and the subatomic particles within them radiate tiny quanta of energetic information. When any aspect of the biofield stagnates, problems occur that can lead to serious blockages and dysfunctions. Think about the physical body, for example. Nothing in it is meant to stagnate. If blood flow is blocked, undesirable clotting follows and can lead to a stroke. If the bowels are blocked from inadequate hydration or lack of movement, systemic toxicity occurs. If the breath is blocked, anoxia sets in, with possible tissue death. Similarly, our vibrational energies are meant to be flowing like a river, constantly renewing and revitalizing body, mind, and spirit.

Varying frequencies are noted in the human biofield with longer waves and slower frequencies occurring in dense tissue, bone, teeth, and the lower chakras. Energies move more rapidly and have a finer vibratory rate in the higher chakras. In assessing the major chakras, an energy practitioner notes that the lower three chakras move more slowly than the upper four and the crown chakra spins most rapidly. The lower chakras are just as important as the upper centers, however, since they are needed to support the evolving consciousness of each human being. The subtle colors of the chakras also reflect the changes in vibratory rates of the electromagnetic spectrum, from the slower red and orange frequencies of the lower chakras to the indigo, violet, and white of the upper centers.

Energy practitioners also discover that the biofield changes in density and vibratory rates as they move their hands from the physical body outward to the edges of the human aura. The first fields are denser, whereas the outer edges vibrate more quickly. Clearing the denser energy layers facilitates energetic balance in the outer layers of the field. Often, disturbances in the more subtle bodies will dissipate spontaneously after denser energies are cleared. In other words, as the healer clears and balances the field, other troubling areas or congestions often dissipate. Since the energy biofield is a hologram, one can work with a single aspect of it and affect the whole field.

Human biofields interact all of the time. To impact another's bio-field in a helpful way, the practitioner must have a higher energetic frequency than the client. The task of the practitioner is to keep his personal field moving at a fast vibratory rate. This is where the disciplines of centering, meditation, and various energy self-care practices that are so highly valued in HT come in to play. Apparently, Jesus and many spiritual teachers like him were able to change others' fields by infusing them with the high-vibration energy of alignment to the Universal Energy Field or Source. Many current energetic practitioners specifically focus on this approach by teaching students to use their breath to draw energy levels to a higher resonance and thereby enhance their biofields.[18]

By providing a higher frequency of vibrant energy for their clients, practitioners may bring about repatterning of a disturbed area, congestion, or energetic blockage. When this occurs spontaneously, it is called a "miracle" because the exact mechanisms lie outside current scientific knowledge. It appears that many patients can repattern their own fields under the right circumstances. It is becoming clear that all healing is actually self-healing. The practitioner is simply the one who facilitates the optimal conditions for the client's self-healing to occur. If the client is depleted and lacks the vitality for clearing his own field, the healer may initially need to help release congestion from the biofield or to break up dysfunctional patterns. After such repairing, the physical body may move to a healthier state. Often, there is a time interval between the practitioner's intervention and perceptible changes in the client's physical body as each person has his individual ways of healing.

Breath is a very important amplifier in energy therapies. The breath acts like a billow, increasing the flow and volume of energy in the healer's field. Pain, for example, can be more easily released if both client and practitioner can exhale emphatically. Rhythmic, deep breaths help keep the practitioner's field clear and charged.

A Theory of Healing

We can often see examples of healing in daily life. Beneath this healing phenomenon, there are processes that can be tracked and studied. In observing psychotherapy clients, hospitalized patients, friends, and family, I (Sharon) began to notice specific patterns in the healing process. There were identifiable stages I could see as individuals dealt with their particular health challenges. These steps or stages are briefly stated as follows:

- **Awareness** of a disturbance

- **Attunement** to the disturbance to evaluate its severity

- **Assessment** of the situation in relation to desired health

- **Setting goals and healing intention** to deal with the condition

- **Alignment** with each goal by seeking out interventions

- **Yielding** to the reality that all possible avenues have been explored and then allowing outcomes to emerge

To elaborate, I have noticed that illness or disturbance brings persons to increased **awareness**. Often, the body has to resort to dysfunction or pain to get needed attention. The distressed person then **attunes** to this disturbance by evaluating the intensity of disruption, noting the change and how this affects functional abilities. Once the client **assesses** the disruption and condition of her health, she sets a **goal and intention** for health in dealing with the condition. (Of course, there are some who choose to deny anything is happening; in this case, the body and mind usually escalate symptoms to get the person's attention.) Once a goal direction is determined, the individual can make specific plans to restore health such as changing diet, increasing exercise levels, seeking outside help, making internal shifts in attitudes or beliefs, and expressing hidden emotions. This phase constitutes **alignment** with one's intention or goal. Chosen actions align with the client's choices. Once this process has begun, there is a "pausing" or "letting go." This **yielding** acknowledges that the person has done everything possible to help herself and now allows outcomes to emerge. Yielding is the magic moment when internal energies can rebalance themselves and restore health. This is not giving up or abandoning one's goal. Instead, it is a softening of the tight hold on demands for specific outcomes.

June's Story

An illustration of the healing process just described is found in the case of June.[19] She experienced her first bout of cancer two years after divorcing her husband, the father of her three grown children. When cancer was detected, she had a lumpectomy and lymph node dissection, which showed no metastases. Within the next two years, she developed liver metastases. June had remarried prior to the reoccurrence and seemed to be doing well in her new relationship. When she met her caregivers, at age fifty-seven, she had awareness but felt stressed over the new diagnosis (*attunement* and *assessment*) and was beginning chemotherapy (*setting goal* and *alignment*). She sought further assistance to deal with her anxiety and met with a biofeedback practitioner to learn relaxation, visualization, temperature and respiration regulation, and postural reeducation (additional forms of *alignment*).

A month into her biofeedback training, the practitioner introduced June to a Healing Touch practitioner who treated her for five sessions *(alignment)* with Magnetic Clearing, the Chakra Connection, and Magnetic Passes (all described in chapter 6) until her energy field became balanced and more vibrant. In the fifth session, June felt pain when the liver was being cleared and then had an actual sensation of a "ball" being removed. During these sessions, June *yielded* to her body's responses. She also sought out emotional support from her husband and her minister *(alignment)*. After the fifth HT session, June reported a re-markable change *(yielding)*: her oncologist was unable to see the metas-tasized "ball" on liver ultrasound scans that had been clearly visible on her original scans. Over the following year, June continued to be free of liver cancer and was diagnosed as "in remission" (another from of *yielding)*. She continued the Healing Touch sessions *(alignment)* in order to keep herself balanced and stress-free.

****

I believe these aspects of the healing process demonstrate how June fully engaged in her self-healing. Helpers and guides can assist, but healing is ultimately in the hands of the client's entire system and alignment with her Higher Power. These aspects of healing correlate closely with the "manifestation process" that is discussed in recent es-oteric literature.[20] The manifestation process includes: identifying the need or issue, setting a specific goal after analyzing one's situation, vi-sualizing the goal, acting on one's behalf, releasing or yielding to God/ Higher Resources, and being open to the possibility of the goal becom-ing manifest.

Sometimes individuals get stuck on one or more aspects of the heal-ing process. For instance, they may focus on a single goal with fierce in-tensity while forgetting to believe in their ability to receive alternative, even novel outcomes. This strong holding on does not allow for ener-gies to shift so new manifestations can happen. In effect, these patients strangle their goals by forgetting to open the door for good to come in. The repatterning toward healthier functioning can occur at both the energetic and physical levels.

After the desired goal is set and available interventions follow, room for hope must be created so new patterns can emerge. This is the yielding and allowing that creates change. Once it has begun and becomes established, the cells of the body can respond and make necessary shifts to a more vibrant pattern.

So far, we have explored features of the human energy system and the unique processes available for client self-healing with the facilitator's support. It remains now for us to learn about some of the most recent scientific findings related to energy therapies and about the research surrounding specific practices such as Healing Touch in the next chapters.

Chapter Notes

1. J. E. Rush, *Towards a General Theory of Healing* (Washington, DC: University Press of America, 1981).

2. I. Veth, *The Yellow Emperor's Classic of Internal Medicine* (Berkeley, CA: University of California Press, 1949).

3. R. Pavek, *Manual Healing Methods: Physical and biofield* (Washington, DC: Report of National Institutes of Health, Office of Alternative Medicine, 1993); and D. Hover-Kramer, *Energetic Impressions of Ancient Egypt* (Port Angeles, WA: Behavioral Health Consultants, 1993).

4. D. Hover-Kramer, *Ancestral Dreams* (Port Angeles, WA: Behavioral Health Consultants, 2001).

5. B. A. Brennan, *Light Emerging: The journey of personal healing* (New York: Bantam Books, 1993).

6. B. A. Brennan, *Hands of Light: A guide to healing through the human energy field* (New York: Bantam, 1987).

7. D. Krieger, *Living the Therapeutic Touch* (New York: Dodd, Mead, 1987).

8. S. Morningstar, *The Art of Wiccan Healing* (Carlsbad, CA: Hay

House, 2005), especially descriptions in the "Leach Book of Bald," 924–946.

9. *Ibid.*

10. J. L. Oschman, *Energy Medicine: The scientific basis* (New York: Churchill Livingstone, 2002).

11. C. Dale, *The Subtle Body: An encyclopedia of your energetic anatomy* (Boulder, CO: Sounds True, 2009).

12. G. E. Schwartz, *The Energy Healing Experiments* (New York: Atria Books, 2007).

13. Dale, *op.cit.*

14. D. Eden, *Energy Medicine for Women* (New York: Tarcher, 2008).

15. Brennan, 1987, *op. cit.*, 42–44.

16. *Ibid.*

17. Eden, *op. cit.*, 147

18. R. Gordon, *Quantum Touch: The power to heal* (Berkeley, CA: North Atlantic Books, 2006).

19. Y. White, Case #2 in S. Scandrett-Hibdon, C. Hardy, and J. Mentgen, *Energetic Patterns: Healing Touch case studies*, Vol. 1 (Lakewood, CO: Colorado Center for Healing Touch, 1999), 9–12.

20. N. D. Walsch, *Happier Than God* (Ashland, Oregon: Emmin Books, (2008); and E. and J. Hicks, *The Law of Attraction* (Carlsbad, CA: Hay House, 2006).

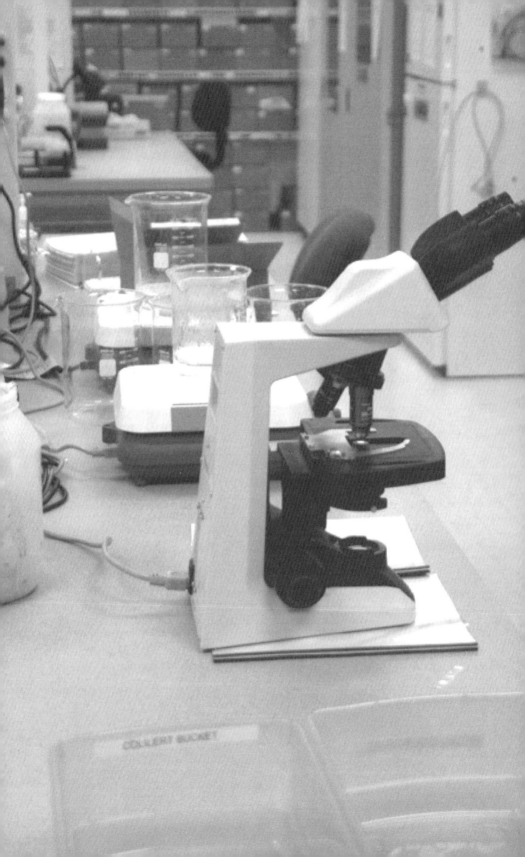

COLILERT BUCKET

Chapter 3

Toward a Scientific Understanding of Energy Healing

James L. Oschman, PhD*

*This chapter is contributed with kind permission by Dr. Oschman and adapted from material first presented in collaboration with Nora Oschman, as "The development of the Living Matrix Concept and its significance for health and healing" at the Science of Healing conference at Kings College, London, March 2009.

The important thing is not to stop questioning. Curiosity has its own reason for existing. One cannot help but be in awe when [one] contemplates the mysteries of eternity, of life, of the marvelous structure of reality.
—Albert Einstein

The science of healing and, with it, understandings of energy-based practices such as Healing Touch are evolving very rapidly. Recent significant developments in health and medical research change our insights into cellular structures and the magnificent interrelated dynamics within living organisms. The living matrix concept summarizes several major advances in our understanding of the nature of cells and tissues in the human body and their relation to human consciousness.

To be specific, the images of the cell and its surroundings in most textbooks (see figure 3.1) are seriously outdated, and this means that students of biology and medicine start with an inaccurate and incomplete picture at the outset of their education. Many confusions and controversies are resolved by the more accurate picture conceptualized in a living matrix.

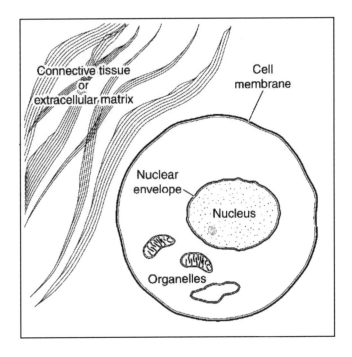

Figure 3.1. Outmoded Model of Human Cell and Surrounding Tissue.

To summarize, figure 3.1 depicts the cell as a bag of solution with a few organelles such as the cell nucleus and mitochondria more or less floating about within it. The cell and its contents form a distinct entity and are separate from the surrounding extracellular matrix or connective tissue.

A more accurate picture (figure 3.2) reveals that the DNA, nucleus, cytoplasm, and extracellular matrix form a continuously interconnected system. The following summarizes the story of how this new picture evolved and the science that has enlivened and energized my work with the living matrix.

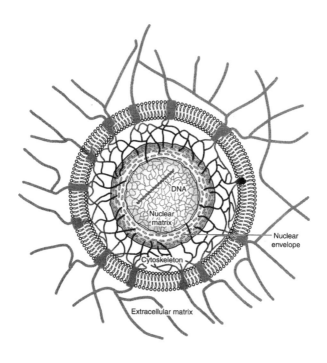

Figure 3.2. Interconnected System of Living Cellular Matrix.

We begin with a story about energy. In 1941, Albert Szent-Györgyi, who had received the Nobel Prize in 1937 for the synthesis of vitamin C, gave the Korányi Memorial Lecture in Budapest, Hungary. His talk was published in both science and nature magazines at a time when his country and all of Europe were descending into the chaos of WWII. The remarkable insight that was the topic of his presentation was that proteins are semiconductors, rather than insulators, as had been thought previously. Semiconductors are intermediate in conductivity between conductors (such as copper wires) and insulators (such as the coverings of electrical cables). In essence, our bodies are composed mainly of materials that are similar in properties to the substances that make possible our modern computers, cell phones, televisions, and so on. He introduced his new ideas as follows:

> "If a great number of atoms is arranged with regularity in close proximity, as for instance, in a crystal lattice, the ... electrons ... cease to belong to one or two atoms only, and belong to the whole system ... A great number of molecules may join to form energy continua, along which energy, viz., excited electrons, may travel a certain distance."[1]

This means that the human body contains free or mobile electrons that can move about within the fabric of the body. These electrons are energetic and can therefore transfer energy and information from place to place. The 1941 report proved to be prophetic, although it was not recognized as such at the time. The area where these ideas have had the most impact is in *nanoelectronics*, the worldwide search for ways of using atoms and molecules as miniature components of electronic circuits. Szent-Györgyi's insight is now recognized as one of the foundations of the modern molecular electronics industry and its development of nanotechnology.[2]

Like most new ideas, the concept that proteins are semiconductors was immediately rejected by the scientific community. Scientists who checked to see if electrons could be conducted through proteins found that the materials were better described as insulators. There was a flaw in their measurements, however. The proteins they studied had been prepared by dehydrating samples taken from living tissues, powdering them, and pressing them into pellets. It was soon discovered that taking the water out of the proteins destroyed their ability to act as semiconductors. The proteins and the water that adheres to them form a two-part semiconducting system. Electrons can move through the proteins and protons can move through the water layers.

Over the years, there has accumulated more and more support for the fact that most of the molecules in living systems have semiconductor properties to some degree. We are also finding that many of the miracles of life rely on the electronic aspects of our cells and tissues.

In 1947, Szent-Györgyi moved to the Marine Biological Laboratory in Woods Hole, Massachusetts, where he established the Institute for Muscle Research. I first learned of his ideas at a fascinating lecture he presented there in 1969. After the lecture I asked a colleague about how these ideas, which were entirely new to me, had been received by the scientific community. I was surprised to learn that the consensus was that, although Szent-Györgyi had done important work in the past, this line of inquiry was unimportant. He was actually too old to do serious science, and he should retire.

Over the years, I asked many of my colleagues to tell me what aspect of this work bothered them, but nobody knew enough about the subject to provide a solid critique. They simply knew it was wrong. I consider this both unscientific and disrespectful. I have learned that this is a typical behavior. Scientists are professional skeptics, and often reject new ideas whether they understand them or not. In his now classic book, *The Structure of Scientific Revolutions*, Thomas Kuhn described how dominant scientific paradigms govern the thinking of entire generations of scientists and teach them what lines of investigation are worthy of study and which are not.[3]

I decided Szent-Györgyi's ideas were fascinating and set out to explore and evaluate them. I now realize that the work of Szent-Györgyi and his colleagues was and continues to be revolutionary and the stuff of a paradigm shift. Like other such ideas, there are a few scientists who fully appreciate the significance of this line of investigation, while the majority are either unaware of it or reject it out of hand. I hope that my writings will help bring these important ideas forward so they can get the attention they deserve.

During my career as a cell biologist and biophysicist, I continued to wonder about electrons, proteins, and electronic biology. Eventually, I had an opportunity to learn more about the subject, when I became a staff scientist at the Marine Biological Laboratory with an office across the hall from Szent-Györgyi's Institute for Muscle Research. Gradually, I came to know the distinguished international family of scientists who worked with or visited Szent-Györgyi's laboratory, and had many valuable conversations with them. In the process, I came to understand what was preventing the scientific community from following this story. To discuss electrons intelligently, one must know a little bit about quantum physics. Few biologists had sufficient understanding of quantum physics to be able to converse about electrons and the electronic aspects of biology. Unfortunately, this is still true today. It is not because quantum physics is difficult or unimportant. In fact, quantum physics goes to the foundation of biology and medicine. Szent-Györgyi and his colleagues were developing a whole new field of research called electronic biology.[4]

One of the reasons for looking deeply into this work was a discovery that took place across the hall from my lab. In collaboration with Peter Gascoyne and Ron Pethig, Szent-Györgyi demonstrated that the protein collagen is a semiconductor.[5] Collagen is the most abundant protein in the world and is the main component of a tissue that has always fascinated me: the connective tissue. This is the material that forms bones, ligaments, tendons, cartilage, and the coverings of bones and muscle known as fascia. The fascia forms the largest system in the body, as it is the system that touches all of the other systems. It can be described as the construction fabric of the physical body. Alfred Pischinger, Hartmut Heine, and their colleagues in Germany referred to the matrix as the "ground regulation system" and the key to health and disease.[6]

These ideas remained in the background of my other research until I was invited to present them to the alternative medicine community, beginning with Rolfers and acupuncturists. In stark contrast to the general scientific community, the practitioners of bodywork, practitioners of energetic and movement therapies, were fascinated with these ideas and found in them the possible validation of their work. Energy and energy flows are fundamental to traditional Oriental medicine and to most complementary and alternative therapies. Acupuncturists suspected that this science was directly related to the flow of qi described in the various forms of East Asian Medicine. It occurred to me that the mental block the biomedical community seemed to have about these therapies might be due in part to the mental block they had about the whole field of electronic biology. I now know that this is substantially correct, and have become dedicated to telling the story summarized here to all who will listen. The living matrix provides a valuable perspective that can connect and integrate very sound approaches to medicine that have been kept separate for too long.

A key piece of the puzzle that led to the living matrix concept came during one of my frequent visits to Cambridge University in England. An English colleague mentioned a remarkable discovery that had taken place at the Medical Research Council Laboratory of Molecular Biology, a short distance south of Cambridge. The date was 1969, and the scientist involved was Mark Bretscher. He had discovered that one of the proteins in the membrane of red blood cells extends across the cell surface, essentially connecting the inside of the cell with the outside. His research on this subject was reported in several scientific journals in 1971.[7] I like mentioning his contribution because it has had profound implications for biology and medicine, but Bretscher's historic discovery is rarely mentioned.

The proteins and arrays of proteins spanning cell membranes have now been widely studied; they are vital to life; and they have profound medical implications. In essence, the family of trans-membrane proteins, which came to be known as integrins, focal adhesion complexes, and so on, completes the "circuitry" of electronic biology. In other words they provide conceptual as well as mechanical, functional, communication, and energetic connections between all that happens inside of cells with the processes taking place everywhere else in the body, and vice versa. Bretscher's work provided the missing piece of a puzzle that goes to the foundation of health and every branch of medicine and therapeutics.

Terms such as *wholistic* (holistic) and *whole systems* now have a precise and detailed picture to go with them: a physical substrate that connects all parts of the organism with all others. Study of the living matrix is providing many details of what we mean when we use the term wholistic or holistic. The living matrix is a conceptual substrate in that it provides a framework for organizing a vast number of discoveries in the fields of cell and molecular biology as well as genetics and epigenetics.[8]

The role of water in relation to the living matrix has been explored by Mae-Wan Ho in collaboration with David Knight. They have suggested that the water associated with collagen constitutes a major part of the acupuncture meridian system and is involved in memory functions. They also proposed that there is a body consciousness, possessing all of the hallmarks of consciousness—sentience, intercommunication, and memory—existing alongside brain consciousness. They propose that *brain consciousness*, which we usually consider to be the only form of consciousness, is embedded within this *matrix consciousness* and is coupled to it. In the context of such a system, the acupuncture meridians and other aspects of human subtle energy are regarded as a specialized information network, based on liquid crystalline resonant pathways, that links and coordinates the various structures and functions within the organism, separate from or along with neural communications.[9] I agree with this perspective and have suggested that the matrix system operates much faster than the nervous system and is responsible for the rapid and coordinated activities of elite athletes and other performers when they are operating "in the zone" of peak achievement.[10]

My first publication on what is now known as the living matrix was in 1981 in an article entitled "The connective tissue and myofascial systems" to describe the interconnectedness of the extracellular and cellular matrices throughout the body. That article, which many came to regard as a classic, and subsequent reports are available through the website, www.energyresearch.us.

A second report was entitled "The structure and properties of ground substances[11] and was dedicated to Dr. Szent-Györgyi in commemoration of his ninetieth birthday. The main new perspective described in that report was that histologists had for many years described "ground substances" in the cell nucleus, the cytoplasm, and extracellular matrices, and mounting evidence was suggesting that all of these fabrics were interconnected.

The whole system, connective tissues, membrane proteins, and the structural fabric of the cell and nucleus are what I referred to as "the connective tissue/cytoskeleton matrix" in a paper presented in January 1993.[12] Later in the same year, we began using the term *living matrix*.[13] The specific sentence in that paper was: "Therefore while we are discussing the cell membrane we keep in mind that we are dealing with a component of a vibratory living matrix, a component that is connected with elements of the cytoskeleton, nuclear matrix, connective tissue, and fascia." The living matrix concept has been widely accepted in the alternative medicine community, as evidenced by more than a thousand references to it on the World Wide Web.

Of great significance was a report from an eminent group at Johns Hopkins School of Medicine under the direction of Dr. Donald Coffey. They were studying the nuclear matrix and its interconnections with both the DNA and with molecules that extend across the nuclear envelope and connect to the cytoskeleton.[14] What this meant was that we could now trace the continuity inward from the extracellular matrix and connective tissues, across the cell surface via the integrins and related molecules first described by Bretscher, throughout the cell cytoplasm via the cytoskeleton, and across the nuclear envelope to the genetic material. In 1991, the same group produced an inspiring report on the way signals propagate through this matrix, which they termed a *tissue tensegrity matrix system*.[15] The tensegrity aspect had evolved from the work of Buckminster Fuller and others.[16] "Tensegrity" is defined as a continuous tensional network (called tendons) supported by a discontinuous set of compressive elements (called struts). The 1991 report by Pienta and Coffey gave precise language and experimental validation to the transfer of energy and information through the living matrix:

> "Cells and intracellular elements are capable of vibrating in a dynamic manner with complex harmonics, the frequency of which can now be measured and analyzed in a quantitative manner ... a tissue-tensegrity matrix system ... is poised to couple the biological oscillations of the cell from the peripheral membrane to the DNA ... [and in the other direction]."[17] (brackets added by the author)

When I discussed these findings with my scientific colleagues, many said that this was no big deal, these connections were well established, and so what? But when I discussed these same findings with alternative practitioners from various therapeutic schools, they were invariably enthusiastic and excited—for they all felt that *this* was the body they had been touching, a body characterized by physical and energetic interconnectedness. This interconnected body appeared to be so different from the reductionist body of Western biomedicine that it was difficult for the two communities to communicate with each other. Perhaps the concept of a living matrix, so thoroughly described by reductionist science, and so much a part of complementary and alternative medicine, can provide a common language for discussion.

My thinking now extends far beyond the story documented here by connecting the physical matrix of the body to the larger biofields that surround the body, and also by taking us into the practical realities of the deeper, submicroscopic levels of quantum reality. This larger scope is vital, for it brings in an appreciation of the broader meaning of "healing energy."

The largest generator of electricity in the body is the heart. It is obvious that the matrix is one system that conducts the "music of the heart" to all parts of our bodies. Research from the Institute of HeartMath has documented the emotional aspects of the harmonics produced by the heart[18] and these harmonics have important roles in healing.[19] The new research on epigenetics is teaching us that the way we think about ourselves and even the words used by the people around us can cause changes at the level of our DNA molecules. It is said that the DNA in every cell in your body is listening to every word you say. From the ideas expressed in this chapter, one can see that the vibratory living matrix probably plays a key role in delivering the vibrations of our words and thoughts to every DNA molecule in our bodies.

The physical living matrix as described also plays key roles as the interface between the matter the body is composed of and the fabric of space that extends in all directions and to all parts of the universe. Indeed, our bodies contain more "empty space" than anything else, and quantum physics tells us that empty space is not, in fact, empty. Space is alive with energy and information and connects us to the deeper levels of consciousness and healing at a distance. It is suspected that study of this interface will someday provide important clues about the nature of the placebo effect and healing through prayer—for one of the most popular and simple quantum models of matter states that electrons and protons and all objects made of them, including our own bodies, are actually formed from waves of energy.[20] It is these waves of energy that give rise to the interconnectedness of all things. Some view the matrix as the transducer that converts our thoughts into material reality, acting through the wave structure of space. While these are interpretations of quantum physics that some physicists find completely irrational, there are other physicists who can tell you that they see these phenomena taking place every day in their laboratories.

In conclusion, it is helpful to think of Healing Touch as a method in which subtle energy via the practitioner's focused consciousness may influence the dynamic matter of the client's living matrix. This cellular matrix itself is also formed from waves of electromagnetic energy. The vibrating matrix of human cells apparently serves as a transducer for the communications received from the healing intention of the HT practitioner.

Much more remains to be discovered in understanding the exact mechanisms of the healing process. In the meantime, let us celebrate what an extraordinary world we live in!

Chapter Notes

1. A. Szent-Györgyi, "The study of energy-levels in biochemistry," *Nature* 148(1941):157–159.

2. N. S. Hush, "An overview of the first half-century of molecular electronics," *Annals of the New York Academy of Sciences* 1006(2006):1–20.

3. T. S. Kuhn, *The Structure of Scientific Revolutions*, 2d ed. (Chicago: University of Chicago Press, 1970).

4. A. Szent-Györgyi, *Introduction to a Submolecular Biology* (New York: Academic Press, 1960); A. Szent-Györgyi, *Bioenergetics* (New York: Academic Press, 1957); A. Szent-Györgyi, *Bioelectronics* (New York, Academic Press, 1968); A. Szent-Györgyi, *Electronic Biology and Cancer* (New York: Marcel Dekker, 1976).

5. P. R. C. Gascoyne, R. Pethig, and A. Szent-Györgyi, "Water structure-dependent charge transport in proteins," *Proceedings of the National Academy of Sciences* 78(1981):261–265.

6. A. Pischinger, *The Extracellular Matrix and Ground Regulation: Basis*

for a holistic biological medicine (Berkeley, CA: North Atlantic Books, 2007).

7. M. S. Bretscher, "A major protein which spans the human erythrocyte membrane," *Journal of Molecular Biology* 59(1971):351–357; also see M. S. Bretscher, "Major human erythrocyte glycoprotein spans the cell membrane," *Nature New Biology* 231(1971):229–232.

8. D. Church, *The Genie in Your Genes: Epigenetic medicine and the new biology of intention* (Santa Rosa, CA: Energy Psychology Press/Elite Books, 2007).

9. M-W. Ho and D. P. Knight, "The acupuncture system and the liquid crystalline collagen fibers of the connective tissues," *American Journal of Chinese Medicine* 26(1998):1–13.

10. J. L. Oschman, *Energy Medicine in Therapeutics and Human Performance* (London: Elsevier, 2003).

11. J. L. Oschman, "Structure and properties of ground substances," *American Zoologist* 24(1983):199–215.

12. J. L. Oschman, "A biophysical basis for acupuncture," Proceedings of the first symposium of the Society for Acupuncture Research, January 23–24, 1993, Rockville, MD.

13. J. L. Oschman and N. Oschman, "Matter, energy, and the living matrix," *Rolf Lines* (magazine of the Rolf Institute in Boulder, CO) 21(October 1993):55–64.

14. R. Berezney and D. S. Coffey, "Isolation and characterization of a framework structure from rat liver nuclei," *Journal of Cell Biology* 73(1977):616–637.

15. K. J. Pienta and D. S. Coffey, "Cellular harmonic information trans-

fer through a tissue tensegrity-matrix system," *Medical Hypotheses* 34(1991):88–95.

16. "Tensegrity" is a naturally occurring construct first recognized and developed by sculptor Ken Snelson and visionary R. Buckminster Fuller. For a detailed discussion, go to Dr. Stephen M. Levin's website, www.biotensegrity.com; accessed June 2009.

17. Pienta and Coffey (1991), *op.cit.*, 88–95.

18. R. McCraty, M. Atkinson, W. A. Tiller, G. Rein, and A. D. Watkins, "The effects of emotions on short-term power spectrum analysis of heart rate variability," *American Journal of Cardiology* 76(1995):1089–1093.

19. J. L. Oschman, *Energy Medicine: The scientific basis* (Edinburgh, UK: Churchill Livingstone/Harcourt, 2000).

20. M. Wolff, Schrödinger's Universe: *Einstein, Waves, and the Origin of the Natural Laws* (Parker, CO: Outskirts Press, 2008).

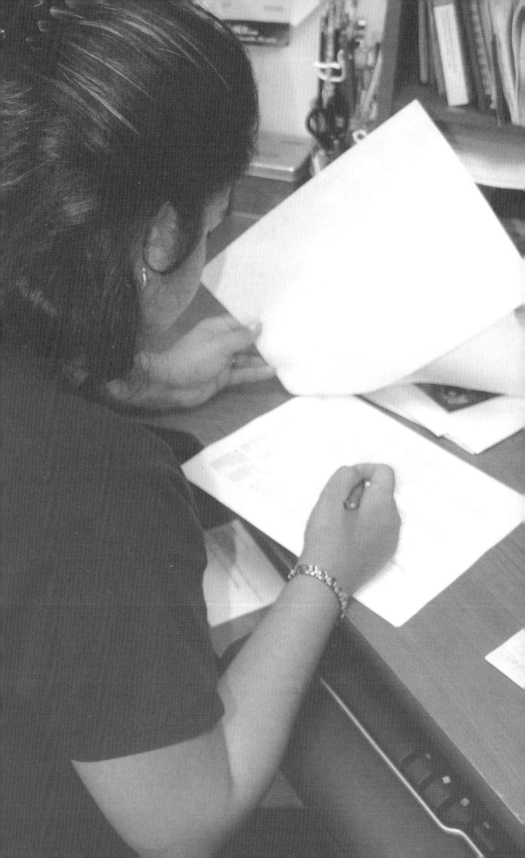

Chapter 4
The Research Basis of Healing Touch

Kathy Moreland Layte, RN, MScN, CNS, HTCP/I

The problems of the world cannot possibly be solved by skeptics or cynics whose horizons are limited by obvious realities. We need men [and women] who can dream of things that never were.

—John Keats

Research involving complementary and alternative medicine therapies has escalated over the past decades to keep pace with the many studies seeking to demonstrate the efficacy of conventional, allopathic treatments. Increasing costs of healthcare, the aging population, accelerated levels of chronic illness, the desire for improved quality of life, fears of sham or fraudulent practices—all these issues contribute to the need for accurate data about complementary, integrative therapies such as Healing Touch.[1]

This chapter will explore research and related issues in Healing Touch. After a brief history of the place of energy-based therapies in complementary modalities, we'll explore research dealing with these modalities, evidence-based practice, and different types of research. The goal is to enlighten research consumers about the criteria for good research. This information will help to answer questions in the following areas:

- The reasons and need for research

- The links between theory and research

- The history of Healing Touch research

- How to become a discerning research consumer

- The best, current examples of research in Healing Touch

- How to access Healing Touch research

Energy-Based Complementary Modalities

In the late 1990s, it was estimated that more than 33 percent of the North American population had used some form of complementary therapy over a twelve-month period and that the use of energy-based therapies increased from 1.3 percent to 3.8 percent between 1990 and 1997.[2] It was also predicted that pursuit of these therapies would continue to rise. Interests and priorities have been influenced by the public's acceptance of energy therapies, their reported positive effects, early research findings, and the possibilities for cost-effectiveness. "In a few decades scientists have gone from a conviction that there is no such thing as energy fields in and around the human body to an absolute certainty that they exist."[3]

The surge of research in complementary and alternative medicine, such as the energy-based therapies taught in the Healing Touch Program, has stimulated interest in evidence-based research. This movement has fostered a drive toward standardization of care to improve efficacy, to focus on health and safety concerns, and to explore the place of complementary therapies in "mainstream" healthcare. Also, there is a need to validate.

Dr. Norman Shealy, well-known physician and founder of the American Holistic Medical Association, and many twenty-first century practitioners following his lead, have declared that energy medicine is indeed the future of medicine.[4] Such vision presses the drive for further research about complementary modalities. The current trend also mandates including information about holistic and complementary practices in the educational programs of mainstream healthcare professionals.

One of the barriers to research in energy-based practices has been the lack of funding for large, well-designed studies. The establishment of the National Institutes of Health's National Center for Complementary and Alternative Medicine (NCCAM) opened the door to greater acceptance and funding for research in five new domains: 1) biologically based practices, 2) manipulative body-based practices, 3) mind-body medicine, 4) whole medical systems, and 5) energy-based therapies. Many special interest groups which previously funded research about conventional therapies for life-threatening illnesses (e.g., cancer, multiple sclerosis, and Alzheimer's disease) are now making funding available for studies in energy medicine and related therapies.

Links Between Research and Science

To understand research involving Healing Touch, it is important to know how current knowledge bases and research are linked. The quest for knowledge is part of being human. One way of expanding knowledge is through research. Western society has long held to a science based on a mechanistic view of biological processes. To measure effectiveness of an intervention, clinical trials, meta-analyses, and systematic reviews are required to be objective. In other words, science and the acceptance of new knowledge rely on testing phenomena under controlled, unbiased circumstances and generalizing from those results to new situations. Some of the most familiar research methods are randomized clinical trials and double-blind studies. Research funding for innovative practices, even those difficult to test, continue to rely on the power given to these time-honored research methods.

In spite of this reverence, it is estimated that only about 30 percent of current medical practice is adequately researched by means of traditional, analytical methods.[5]

As thinking has changed and the limitations of traditional research approaches has surfaced, willingness to consider other methods of research has emerged.[6] These methods of research do not negate the importance of traditional approaches but instead support knowledge development that is directed by the kinds of questions being asked. For example, a question exploring the *impact of a method* such as effects of HT treatment on arthritis pain requires a different research method than one that asks about the *lived inner experience* of a person receiving HT interventions for arthritis pain.

Since the early 1990s, evidence-based practice has identified research approaches that include both observer expertise and understanding of patient needs as a basis for clinical decision-making.[7] Evidence-based practice considers all types of research evidence: the skill level of the practitioner, availability of resources, and client characteristics including their state of health, personal realities, values, preferences, and capacity for self-care (figure 4.1).

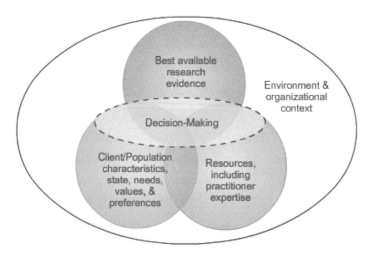

Figure 4.1 Criteria for Selection of the Best Research Methods.

Research confirms that patient outcomes are 28 percent better when care is based on qualitative research that includes the criteria named here rather than care that is based on more traditional quantitative research.[8] Qualitative research promotes dialogue between practitioners and clients about their preferences to bring effective symptom relief.

Barriers to such evidence-based research include lack of access to library search engines, lack of exploratory skills, lack of education in critical appraisal of studies, and insufficient support for innovation in established institutions. In addition, investigators themselves may hold negative attitudes toward complementary therapies. Working collaboratively takes time, patience, knowledge, and finances. Collaboration is therefore more challenging than running simple statistical analyses, in spite of the reality that overall outcomes are better.

Reviewing the best available research evidence requires a review of the "strength" of the evidence through a hierarchical approach. Figure 4.2 demonstrates this hierarchy. What this means is that all forms of research are valued in a best-practice approach, but the types of studies closer to the top of the pyramid in the figure represent the best available research evidence

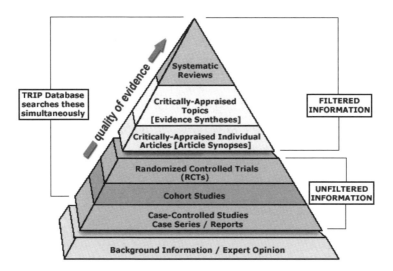

Figure 4.2. The Evidence-based Hierarchy of Research Designs.

(In June 2009, Figures 4.1 was retrieved from http://www.ebbp. org/ebbp.html and 4.2 was retrieved from http://demo.libguides. com/content.php?pid=9169&sid=97199.)

A recent study showed that conventional physicians were much more likely to consider research results very important or "very useful" in their clinical decision-making whereas physician providers of complementary therapies were more likely to say that patient preferences were essential.[9] The latter group were also much more likely to rank research results as "least important," whereas conventional caregivers were much more likely to rate patient preferences as being of little consequence.

Energy-Based Therapy Research

A large number of studies in energy-based therapies including Healing Touch have been conducted. In spite of significant results in many of these studies, the need for greater attention to design detail is consistently mentioned in all reviews of them.[10] This is a common issue in complementary therapy research. Numerous authors[11] concerned with the progress of energy-based research have encouraged researchers to develop clear designs that consider such items as appropriate sample sizes, elimination of biases, appropriate randomization of subjects, control of variables that may impact the therapy, appropriate placebo controls, use of comparison mock practices, concomitant therapies ,and use of expert practitioners. Complex tensions need to be held to assure both rigor and relevance in studying holistic therapies such as Healing Touch. Experts in this kind of research have developed guidelines for assessing and assuring that specific research design and reporting strategies have been used in the execution of a study.[12] Professionals with interest in energy-oriented research have also formed organizations such as the International Society for the Study of Subtle Energies and Energy Medicine and the Institute of Noetic Sciences (contact information in appendix E).

Persons interested in Healing Touch may or may not have a background in research review. Students of the HT Program are introduced to the importance of research and recent studies that support the work in the various levels of the program. It is important for practitioners to understand the recency of HT research and the further need for validating research.

The History of Healing Touch Research

Recognition and support of research of Healing Touch began in the mid-1990s with encouragement from the Healing Touch Program founding group members. Before that time, practitioners relied heavily on the work of Therapeutic Touch research to support their work. As with many energy-based therapies, it was often difficult to tell if cited results were influenced by treatment error or study design flaws.

In 1994, with the support of a grant from the American Holistic Nurses Association, the first Healing Touch research director was appointed and the first directory of Healing Touch studies was developed. Resources and experts in research are now available to provide a variety of services and consultation to those interested in understanding, conducting, and supporting HT research. The HTP website www.HealingTouchProgram.com contains helpful information about HT research as well as experts' services. Newsletter articles are available about established research and issues identified for further study. Also, computerized search engines to find specific research topics have simplified finding reputable published resources and studies.

Links Between Research and Theory

Theory and research are foundational blocks of practice. Theories drive research, and research, in turn, drives development of theory.

Theories are descriptions of interrelated philosophical concepts and form the foundation of a practice that can be evaluated by its practitioners. Thus, theory and research are interdependent and they rely on each other.

For example, Watson's Theory of Human Caring, considered so congruent with HT practice, involves the concept of intentionality and heart-centered practice.[13] Research could be developed to explore the psychological or physical impact of being a heart-centered practitioner. Another study could be designed to evaluate whether being heart-centered and intentional really makes a difference in treatment outcomes. Healing Touch practice is also congruent with humanistic philosophies from other disciplines and the work of nurse theorists such as Margaret Newman, Martha Rogers, and Florence Nightingale. These theories can be tested and evaluated with both qualitative and quantitative research methods.

The Need for Good Research

Research is one of the best ways to explore the possible effects of Healing Touch practice. Research is also highly valued by healthcare agencies, schools for healthcare professionals, and by the wary people who believe that complementary therapies are a sham without a real scientific base.

HT practitioners are often asked:

- How do you know this therapy works?
- What evidence supports this practice?
- How do you know which health issues can best be addressed?
- What is the experience of people who get this therapy?
- What theories and research support this work?

In my experience, understanding good studies answers these questions and validates HT practice.

Practitioners of Healing Touch may or may not need research to "do the work." Knowing about research is essential, however, when the need for validation arises. To an unskilled eye, almost any study could be seen as the "proof" to promote HT, particularly in conventional healthcare settings. To some extent, all studies are worthwhile as they are part of the knowledge puzzle. Studies can be problematic, however, if they are not reviewed adequately, are shared prematurely, or are presented in the wrong contextual settings.

In spite of preventative screening and careful scrutiny, poorly designed or poorly conducted studies are still being reported and/or published. This entices unwary persons to enthusiastically proclaim questionable results.

A recent example of a research fiasco is a study of Therapeutic Touch called the Rosa Study.[14] It raised concerns about the credibility of Therapeutic Touch and other energy-based healing methods. Public media and skeptical healthcare practitioners embraced the negative results of the study and proclaimed energy practices as fraudulent without looking more closely at the underlying motivation of the principal investigators or reviewing the flawed design of the study. Publication of study in the Journal of the *American Medical Association (JAMA)* was deemed sufficient to establish legitimacy of the study. Further review of the study uncovered, among other things, many serious design flaws and reporting discrepancies.[15] *JAMA's* editors were duly embarrassed in front of their extensive readership.

Types of Research

In general, there are two kinds of research: *quantitative* and *qualitative*. Quantitative studies are the types of studies that tend to look for statistical evidence that a treatment is effective for a specific condition. As mentioned, the majority of the scientific community consider these types of studies the best form of research. To be worthy of review, they require control of variables, random assignment of the recipients to different groups, large numbers of participants and/or exposures to the treatment, blinding of the recipients to the purpose of the project, and complex statistical analysis. Only careful scrutiny determines if controls and research conditions are met.

Qualitative studies, on the other hand, generally strive to elicit descriptions of an experience and its meaning for the person. They are not used to determine effectiveness or efficacy of interventions but rather look for themes and relationships. These types of studies do not require large samples and don't control for variables. They do follow clearly outlined processes so they can be replicated. Qualitative studies help elicit important understanding of human themes that cannot be quantified such as spirituality, caring, hope, loss, and psychological insights.

Mixed methods studies, incorporating both quantitative and qualitative concepts, are increasingly popular. Mixed methods explore experience with controlled variables to find more comprehensive conclusions to research questions. They also look for inconsistencies between measured outcomes and participants' descriptions of their experience. Evidence-based practice supports the use of mixed methods to maintain the narrative component of holistic therapies.

Pilot studies are smaller-scale feasibility studies used in quantitative designs to troubleshoot design difficulties of a future, larger study. They are often used to demonstrate the outcome possibilities to acquire funding for a larger study. By working out flaws and fine-tuning a study's design, researchers save time and money. Many studies in Healing Touch are considered pilot studies because they have small sample sizes. Without a large sample size, it is difficult to determine if significance in the effect of the intervention was achieved or if the results were due to chance alone.

Evaluating Research

Given that there are more than ninety completed studies involving HT, how can one decide which studies best support Healing Touch? Asking the following questions will help you to be an effective consumer of research information:

- **Are there obvious concerns in design such as small sample size, lack of controls for bias, poor blinding of study participants, or use of a mock practice?**

- **Is the study published in a reputable, peer-reviewed journal?** Many reputable studies have been done as part of graduate studies but have not been published. Peer-reviewed, published studies generally carry more weight in the scientific community. It means that the design, conduct, and reporting of the results have been carefully scrutinized by experts in the field. Pilot studies can be published and are valuable contributions to science as long as they are acknowledged as such.

- **Are the authors making outlandish claims about the findings? Are they claiming that their findings are applicable to other groups other than the one tested?** Few reputable researchers would ever say that their research "proves" anything or that their results demonstrate effectiveness for another treatment group. At best, they suggest that the effect was not due to chance alone (i.e., it had statistical significance) or that their findings support a previous study. In qualitative designs, any claims that the meanings elicited by the participants will be the same for other people should raise suspicion. Think of research studies as pieces of a puzzle, supporting or refuting bigger phenomena. Even systematic reviews and meta-analyses are limited by the number and quality of the studies surveyed.

- **Does the discussion section of the paper explain whether or not statistical significance was achieved?** A reputable research paper does not always have to find statistical significance. If the design of the research was of high quality, the research can still answer questions about the phenomena studied. Collective information gathered from many studies can demonstrate significant results. The Cochrane Database, for example, available through public library systems, is a collection of systematic reviews of studies in all areas of healthcare. Experienced researchers review large collections of studies and determine if there is sufficient evidence to support changes in medical practice.

- **Have the investigators been true to their research methods?** Different types of research are needed to answer varied research questions, and differing methods require alternative approaches to data evaluation. Deviation from these methods or an inability to follow the "trail" of research conduct casts suspicion on the results.

- **If the study is a pilot study, have investigators made suggestions for refinement of future designs? Did they fully explain the reasons for their conclusions?**

- **Do the investigators have special interests in finding the results they did?** Most investigators are heavily invested in the interest area they are studying. What is important in reviewing the credibility of a study and its results is to know how investigator bias was avoided.

The Best Recent Studies in Healing Touch

As mentioned, a great deal of research is being done involving Healing Touch therapies, and entire journals are devoted to reporting research in complementary therapies. Many HT studies have been funded by internationally recognized organizations and special interest groups. Published and unpublished studies and pilot studies have been conducted to look at the impact of HT methods on diseases and conditions such as cancer, heart disease, immunological and endocrine disorders, headaches, postoperative wounds, pediatric conditions, alcoholism, menopausal syndromes, and dementia in numerous settings including hospitals, outpatient clinics, and hospices. Symptoms explored have included pain, fatigue, depression, anxiety, agitation, stress, and nausea in various aspects of the human life span.

A directory of studies that have been conducted in relation to Healing Touch covers many pages and can be found on the Internet.[16] New consumers need to review that list with a discerning eye and ask the aforementioned questions to look for the best evidence that supports HT practice. Despite design flaws, the bulk of evidence suggests that positive outcomes are occurring with HT and that these results are due to more than chance.

Many studies conducted in HT have not been published or reported. Copies of these studies can be requested through academic libraries. Summary abstracts can also be obtained through search engines of dissertation abstracts or through Google Scholar.

Following are examples of well-conducted Healing Touch research that supports its principles and meets most of the criteria I noted previously. Because there is an increasing number of well-conducted studies, space constraints permit me to highlight only the current ones with which I think the interested public will want to be familiar.

Quantitative Studies

A dedicated group of cardiac care professionals enrolled 237 study subjects who were undergoing coronary artery bypass surgery to evaluate whether Healing Touch therapy would improve six different outcomes in comparison with two other groups who did not receive HT.[17] The items for comparison were: 1) length of hospital stay; 2) incidence of postoperative atrial fibrillation, a heart-rate irregularity common after bypass surgery; 3) use of anti-nausea medication; 4) use of pain medication; 5) functional status measured by ability to move and care for self; and 6) psychological anxiety states. Each of the participants received the standard care provided in the hospital. Those in the study group received HT the day before surgery, immediately prior to surgery, and the day after surgery. The researchers found no significant decrease in the use of pain medication, anti-nausea medication or incidence of atrial fibrillation between the groups. They did, however, find significant improvement in anxiety relief and a reduced length of stay by almost one full day in the group who received HT treatments compared to the other groups. The results of this well-conducted study demonstrated significant cost savings for the hospital and led to implementation of a new policy for all patients to receive HT prior to cardiac surgery.

In another good example of a well-designed clinical trial, researchers explored the impact of HT on the reported health-related quality of life of women receiving HT during radiation treatment for gynecological or breast cancers.[18] The sample consisted of sixty-two newly diagnosed women who were randomly assigned to receive either HT or a mock form of therapy. The participants received the treatments weekly for a total of six weeks immediately after their radiation treatment. The participants were not aware of which treatments they were receiving because practitioners were behind a screen. Those receiving HT reported improvement in all nine areas of quality of life measured, with statistical significance noted for enhanced vitality, pain reduction, and improved physical functioning in comparison to those who received mock forms of therapy.

This study addresses many of the research study design challenges that confront those who conduct energy therapy research. The use of mock therapy, for example, continues to be debatable since energy field theory suggests that all practitioners have the ability to affect outcomes through their presence, which brings changes to a client's electromagnetic biofield.[19]

Qualitative Studies

Although not published, three phenomenological studies have been conducted exploring the lived experience of women receiving HT therapy during their cancer treatments.[20] All three studies revealed consistent themes of a caring connection between clients and their HT practitioners. Clients also noted increased recognition of personal strengths, ability to meet self-care needs, and altered perceptions of their environment. These enhanced perceptions helped the women to get through the treatment protocols without psychological distress.

A Mixed Method Study

Mixed methods designs are those that explore phenomena with analysis of qualitative and quantitative data. This research method is becoming increasingly popular as it recognizes that clinical trials cannot answer all types of questions. It also recognizes that self-report questionnaires or scales, often used in quantitative approaches, have limitations and may not reveal the richness of people's internal experiences.

A mixed methods design explored whether HT enhanced health[21] and studied salivary secreted immunoglobulin A (sIgA), a protein in the body thought to be related health enhancement, which was recorded before and after treatment. Other data gathered qualitative information about current stress levels and perceptions of health. The sample consisted of twenty-two clients who had never experienced HT. All of the participants experienced three types of conditions: no treatment, HT alone, and HT plus music and guided imagery over a period of two weeks. Statistically significant results and review of the qualitative data established that HT enhanced health through raised immunoglobulin concentrations and lowered perceptions of stress and pain relief. Common themes from the participants were relaxation, increased awareness of others, a meaningful relationship with the practitioner, positive mood changes, and an improvement of 55 percent for those who had pain. The researchers deduced that the results were not due to chance or placebo effect.

A Pilot Study

A recent pilot study investigated the effect of Healing Touch on anxiety and five different physiological measures (heart rate, blood pressure, muscle tension, skin conductance, and skin temperature) with thirty healthy adults using a convenience sampling technique.[22] Physiological data were collected at three intervals of ten minutes before intervention, thirty minutes during the Healing Touch treatment, and ten minutes post treatment. During the course of the treatment, changes were observed for all psychological and physiological measures, suggestive of relaxation and a decrease in psychological anxiety with the exception of muscle tension, which remained constant. Qualitative data were also collected and participants reported feeling "energized," "safe," "comforted," "cool," "tingly," and "light." Results suggest that Healing Touch treatment is associated with both physiological and psychological relaxation. As a result of the pilot study findings, a larger study was designed with a control group and is currently being completed.

Accessing HT Research

Whether you are an experienced researcher or a novice, your best resource for finding reputable research studies involving HT is to contact your local library, your local college/university library, or the health science library of your local healthcare facility. The Healing Touch Program's online *Energy Magazine*, and other newsletters routinely report research studies in a user-friendly way to inform practitioners and interested parties. Searching the Internet through search engines such as Google Scholar can also help you find resources and titles of reputable articles. Sometimes a brief abstract outlining study design and findings can be found without cost. Some libraries charge a fee for full text research articles because they tend to be lengthy. Contacting HTP, www. HealingTouchResearch.com, or other agencies involved in energy-based therapies can be helpful in finding additional resources.

—⁓⁓—

Having knowledge of what to look for in research and comprehending its results can greatly enhance understanding of HT practice. Understanding research helps practitioners explain themselves to others when practicing with families or bringing this work into healthcare facilities, academic institutions, or businesses. Actually participating in research is another fascinating avenue for practitioners and provides a path for widening acceptance of HT practices.

Chapter Notes

1. S. M. Zick, "Bridging CAM practice and research: Teaching CAM practitioners about research methodology," *Alternative Therapies in Health and Medicine* 10 (2004):50–56.

2. D. M. Eisenberg, R. B. Davis, S. L. Ettner, et al., "Trends in alternative medicine use in the United States, 1990–1997: Results of a follow-up national survey," *Journal of the American Medical Association* 280(1998):1569–1575.

3. J. Oschman, *Energetic Medicine: The scientific basis* (London: Churchill Livingstone, 2000).

4. D. Feinstein and D. Eden, "Six pillars of energy medicine: Clinical strengths of a complementary paradigm," *Alternative Therapies in Health and Medicine* 14(2008):44–54.

5. D. G. Altman, "The scandal of poor medical research," *British Medi-*

cal Journal 308(1994):283–284.

6. B. A. Carper, "Fundamental patterns of knowing in nursing," *Advances in Nursing Science* 1(1978):13–23; M. K. Jacobs-Kramer and P. L. Chinn, "Perspectives on knowing," *Scholarly Inquiry for Nursing Practice* 2(1988):129–139; M. C. Silva, J. M. Sorrell, and C. D. Sorrell, "From Carper's patterns of knowing to ways of being: An ontological philosophical shift in nursing," *Advances in Nursing Science* 18(1995):1–13; J. Richardson, "Evidence-based complementary medicine: Rigor, relevance, and the swampy lowlands," *Journal of Alternative and Complementary Medicine* 8(2002):221–223.

7. D. L. Sackett, S. E. Straus, W. S. Richardson, W. M. C. Rosenberg, and R. B. Haynes, *Evidence-Based Medicine: How to practice and teach EMB* (London: Churchill Livingstone, 1997).

8. B. M. Melnyk and C. M. Baldwin, "Evidence-based practice," in B. M. Dossey (ed.), *Holistic Nursing: A handbook for practice* (Boston: Jones & Bartlett, 2009), 695–707.

9. J. C. Tilbert, F. A. Curlin, T. J. Kaptchuk, et al., "Alternative medicine research in clinical practice: A U.S. national survey," *Archives of Internal Medicine* 169(2009):670–677.

10. D. W. Wardell and K. F. Weymouth, "Review of studies of Healing Touch," *Journal of Nursing Scholarship* 36(2004):147–154; J. Engebretson and D. W. Wardell, "Energy-based modalities," *Nursing Clinics of North America* 42(2007):243–259; C. Crawford, A. G. Sparber, and W. B. Jonas, "A systematic review of the quality of research on hands-on and distance healing: Clinical and laboratory studies," *Alternative Therapies in Health and Medicine* 9(2003):A96–A104; P. S. So, Y. Jiang, and Y. Qin, "Touch therapies for pain relief in adults," *Cochrane Database of Systematic Reviews* 4(2008), art. no.: CD006535. DOI: 10.1002/14651858.CD006535.pub2.

11. A. L. Ai, C. Peterson, B. Gillespie, et al., "Designing clinical trials on energy healing: Ancient art encounters medical science," *Alternative Therapies in Health and Medicine* 7(2001):83–90; S. L. Warber, A. Gordon, B. W. Gillespie, M. Olson, and N. Assefi, "Standards for conducting clinical biofield energy healing research," *Alternative Therapies in Health and Medicine* 9:(2003):A54–A64; I. Boutron, D. Moher, D. G. Altman, K. F. Schulz, and P. Ravaud, "Extending the CONSORT statement to randomized trials on non-pharmacologic treatment: Explanation and elaboration." *Annals of Internal Medicine* 148(2008):295–309.

12. W. B. Jonas and R. A. Chez, "The role and importance of definitions and standards in healing research," *Alternative Therapies in Health and Medicine* 9(2003):A5–A9.

13. J. Watson, *Postmodern Nursing and Beyond* (New York: Churchill Livingstone, 1999).

14. L. Rosa, E. Rosa, L. Sarner, and S. Barrett, "A close look at therapeutic touch," *Journal of the American Medical Association* 279(1998):1005–1010.

15. T. Cox, "A nurse-statistician reanalyzes data from the Rosa therapeutic touch study," *Alternative Therapies in Health and Medicine* 9(2003):58–64.

16. D. W. Wardell, "Research Survey within Healing Touch International," 2008, http://www.healingtouchinternational.org/index.php?option=com_content&task=view&id=61&Itemid=178.

17. J. MacIntyre, J. Hamilton, T. Fricke, W. Ma, S. Mehle, and M. Matt, "The efficacy of Healing Touch in coronary artery bypass surgery recovery: A randomized clinical trial," *Alternative Therapies in Health and Medicine* 14(2008):24–32.

18. C. A. Cook, J. F. Guerrerio, and V. E. Slater, "Healing Touch and quality of life in women receiving radiation treatment for cancer: A randomized controlled trial," *Alternative Therapies in Health and Medicine* 10(2004):34–41.

19. V. Slater, "Summary of energy healing, healers, and the one being healed," in B. M. Dossey (ed.), *Holistic Nursing: A handbook for practice* (Boston: Jones & Bartlett, 2009), 647–s694.

20. C. Christiano, "The lived experience of healing touch with cancer patients" [master's thesis], Florida International University in Miami, 1997; D. Kopecki, "The lived experience of women with breast cancer" [master's thesis], Sage Graduate School, Albany, NY, 2001; K. Moreland, "The lived experience of receiving the chakra connection of women with breast cancer who are receiving chemotherapy: A phenomenological study" [master's thesis], University of Windsor, Ontario, Canada, 1998.

21. D. S. Wilkinson, P. L. Knox, J. E. Chatman, T. L. Johnson, et al., "The clinical effectiveness of Healing Touch," *Alternative and Complementary Medicine* 8(2002):33–47.

22. J. A. Maville, J. E. Bowen, G. Benham, "Effect of Healing Touch on stress perception and biological correlates," *Holistic Nursing Practice* 22(2008):103–110.

Section II

Description of Healing Touch Practices and Coursework

Chapter 5

Major Concepts and Principles of the Healing Touch Curriculum

Cynthia Hutchison, DNSc, RN, HTCP/I*

*Both Cynthia and Dorothea wish to express deep appreciation to Toni Adsit-Wilson for her expertise in sharing Jean Watson's theoretical material for this chapter.

Never doubt that a small group of thoughtful, committed citizens can change the world. Indeed, it's the only thing that ever has.

—Margaret Mead

For each session, practitioners of Healing Touch utilize a ten-step sequence that is guided by specific concepts and principles for developing effective practice. To begin, we'll look at an overview of the major concepts guiding HT practice and then we'll explore the ten-step sequence.

Conceptual Underpinnings for the Healing Touch Program Curriculum

The following concepts and principles are woven throughout the basic HTP curriculum from Level One through Level Five. Each level is usually taught in a weekend workshop and the time between classes permits integration of learning. The typical student focused on course completion usually takes about eighteen to twenty-four months to graduate but because of the flexibility intrinsic in the HT Program structure, students can take several years to complete the process.

Dr. Jean Watson's Theory of Human Caring supports and enhances the material. As students progress through each level of the curriculum, theoretical concepts come to life. Some students have a natural affinity for hands-on healing work because of their previous life experiences, whereas others describe the first class and its learning activities as an opening to a whole new life adventure.

In this portion of the chapter, we'll discuss:

- Preparation of the practitioner

- Principles of healing

- Applications of Watson's Theory of Caring to Healing Touch practice.

Preparation of the Practitioner

Learning the basics of centering, grounding, and attuning serves practitioners well for the rest of their lives. These concepts are integral to holistic practice because they set the stage for healing of body, mind, and spirit for both client and practitioner. Practitioners who are centered exude qualities that make others around them feel safe, accepted, and confident; this establishes the rapport for the therapeutic relationship.

Centering is the practitioner's art of being fully present to the client while at the same time being focused within and receptive to intuition. The ability to center and quiet oneself is a primary dimension of caring. Focusing the breath to come into the present moment assists the centering process while ongoing practices of meditation enhance and deepen centering as part of a lifelong learning process.

Grounding is effected by connecting to the earth, being present in the body, and feeling inner balance. It is important to "ground self ... to provide comforting, soothing, calming acts."[1] Practitioners ground themselves before, during, and after giving treatments to be fully present and alert, and to protect themselves from the possibility of taking on client symptoms. Practitioners also ground clients in various ways to ensure that the client is in the "here and now" before leaving a session.

Attuning is the process of consciously entering into an energetic connection with the client through the use of light touch and/or setting healing intention. Practitioners center and ground themselves prior to implementing any hands-on methods.

In addition to these preparations, HT practitioners hold the sense of their presence to express compassion, humility, and nonjudgment. Being fully present with others is much more than implementing techniques. Watson tells us, "Caring begins with being present, open to compassion, mercy, gentleness, loving-kindness, and equanimity toward and with self before one can offer compassionate caring to others."[2] HT instructors often speak to their students of coming from the heart as well as the head. Although intellectual, mental knowledge is required to be effective in communication skills, HT practice also entails activating one's sense of warmhearted kindness toward the client. The practitioner's neutral, nonjudgmental attentiveness builds clients' trust, which facilitates the healing process.

Creation of a mutually sensed safe, special space is essential. "This view brings us face-to-face with the mystery and infinity of humanity itself and with all life processes ... we understand more deeply the sacredness of caring ... each act we commit is part of a larger whole."[3] Showing respect through words and actions, taking adequate time, giving eye contact, presenting the body language of truly listening, and caring about what is said—all these help to create the focused environment for the entire interaction. A sacred, safe space has been created when clients feel serenity despite outward environmental distractions and they have described the feeling of being within a cocoon of protection and peace. The transpersonal caring-healing model of Watson was born from the assumption that "Caring accepts and holds safe space for people to seek their own wholeness of being and becoming."[4]

Healing Touch practitioners are encouraged to "walk their talk" by engaging in an active program of personal body-mind-spirit care. Practitioners are expected to receive HT regularly, to participate in ongoing continuing education, and to seek personal growth activities. It is not possible to give of oneself effectively without taking time to be reflective of one's own life. Many people drawn to the healing arts have a strong desire to serve others but may lack consciousness about the importance of honoring themselves. Self-care is explained by Watson as "Cultivating one's own spiritual practices and transpersonal self, going beyond ego-self (working with heart-centeredness)."[5] To practice care for self, she suggests practices of self-reflection; use of discernment; developing meaningful rituals for practicing gratitude, forgiveness, surrender, and compassion; transforming tasks into caring-healing interactions; acceptance of self and others; demonstration of interest in others; and valuing the intrinsic goodness of self and others.

Practitioners of Healing Touch also know and adhere to the HTP Code of Ethics (given in appendix B). Students are introduced to these concepts from the onset of the first class. The behaviors described in these documents are essential for those who want to align themselves with the professional and ethical foundations of the Healing Touch Program.

Principles of Healing

In essence, the Healing Touch practitioner becomes a conduit for the flow of Universal Energy. Practitioners do not give up their own energy; instead, they constantly receive more energy when treating others. The practitioner connects to Source Energy through centering and grounding, tapping into the unlimited supply of energy in the Universe. After a session, practitioners should feel more balanced, connected, and energized than before because of this connection. Facilitating the flow of the vital life force to the client enhances the field of the practitioner as well. To use a metaphor, a tree receives the unlimited supply of solar energy from the sun in order to grow. As the tree nurtures new seedlings or extends its roots, its vital life force also expands.

Another aspect of practitioner preparation is letting go of attachments to outcomes in order to set intention for the client's highest good. Watson explains, "Each caring act seeks to hold an intentional consciousness of caring. This energetic, focused consciousness of caring and authentic presenting has the potential to change the field of caring, thereby potentiating healing and wholeness."[6] The desire to help clients/patients feel better is a natural tendency among those involved in the healing arts. Being nonattached to specific outcomes is easier said than done, especially when working with a loved one or attempting to demonstrate the effectiveness of an intervention! Practitioners must learn to trust that healing at some level will take place even if there is no apparent change. By holding intention for the client's highest good, practitioners also release ego tendencies to accept credit or take responsibility for outcomes. Understandably, such caring nonattachment requires ongoing personal commitment.

The difference between curing and healing becomes evident when we acknowledge the multidimensional nature of each person. For example, a heart transplant patient may recover from surgery, that is, experience a physical cure, but still be in need of emotional, mental, and spiritual *healing*. Someone who dies of cancer does not receive physical *cure* but may still experience emotional, mental, and spiritual *healing*. Healing is used in HT as a broad term to describe movement toward optimal well-being in all possible dimensions of the person.

Another important principle is the idea of "effortless effort." This means there is no need to push or direct the vital life force—it knows where it is needed in the client's energy system. Learning to relax and let go while giving an intervention comes easier to some students than others. Some struggle with the paradoxical idea of "effortless effort," which only makes sense when practitioners understand they hold the safe, sacred space that "allows" healing to happen while they add specific hand gestures, mental focus, and spiritual alignment. Therefore, *effort* is continuously aimed at maintaining the healing space. Holding the light for healing has to be learned and practiced since practitioners' life cycles, health states, and current events can greatly influence personal concentration.

Human energy flow has its own divine intelligence. Practitioners serve as conduits for this flow on behalf of the client. Remembering this principle releases the pressure of attempting to direct outcomes. It prevents practitioners from letting their ego needs get in the way.

Following the energy and how it moves in the client improves with practice and development of intuition. Practitioners learn to use their hands and hearts during a session, but they also learn how to live more fully. When one is truly present in the moment, one can sense guidance and inner wisdom. Trusting intuitive knowing is part of the "effortless" intention. The more one stays connected to the present moment, the more one can develop perceptive insights.

Breath supports the healer. Focused breathing is a way to release *that which does not serve the person* on exhalation and *bring in that which is new—nourishment, light, health, ideas*—on inhalation. Focus on the breath helps practitioners to come into the present moment, the Now, as an easy way to begin practicing the art of presence. Classroom meditations teach practitioners how to center and release distractions.

Memories, emotions, and traumas can be held in the client's physical body or energy field and may be released during HT treatments. Clients often report relief from ongoing symptoms of past trauma. Such relief can occur with basic HT methods as well as specific methods taught in the advanced practice Trauma Release (described in chapter 12).

There are many paths and methods of healing. Healing Touch is *one* effective way for actualizing Watson's concept of creating the healing environment "at all levels (physical as well as nonphysical, subtle environment of energy and consciousness) whereby wholeness, beauty, comfort, dignity, and peace are potentiated."[7] From the many available methods and paths to healing, individuals determine which path best suits them for their own self-healing and personal growth.

With more than twenty years of history, HT has proven itself as an effective caring philosophy and healing method. HT practitioners honor all paths of healing that empower recipients, respect all belief systems, and embrace the desire to continue their learning.

Applications of Watson's Theory of Caring to Healing Touch Practice

Watson suggests practitioners respectfully assist with the basic needs of clients while at the same time "[holding an intentional, caring consciousness of touching and working with the embodied spirit of another, honoring unity of Being: allowing for spirit-filled connection."[8] HT methods are given with heart-centered focus rather than dedication to technical perfection. Though practitioners respect specific HT methods and guidelines, intention and intuitive caring take precedence. Caring intention will reach clients when the practitioner maintains the safe space, holds intention for highest good, and works with compassion.

Practitioners learn to hold positive thoughts about their clients while they are in the therapeutic relationship. Clients are also encouraged to hold positive thoughts for themselves through affirmations, mantras, prayers, or images of increased health.

Watson believes, "We have to treat ourselves with loving-kindness and equanimity, gentleness, and dignity before we can accept, respect, and care for others within a professional caring-healing model."[9] It is clear that caring as taught in HT promotes self-growth, self-knowledge, self-control, and self-healing processes in the practitioner. "To engage in healing our self and our relationship with each other and beyond, the practices of *Forgiveness, Offering Gratitude, and Surrendering* to higher/deeper source for consolation, creativity, insight, and heart-centered action is a way to begin."[10] Because of these insights, there is much emphasis in the HT program on practitioner self-care, which is discussed further in chapter 13.

Practitioners acknowledge that they are not the cause of healing but serve to facilitate a process that really takes place between the client and the client's Higher Power. Through the practitioner's ability to set positive intention while the hands interact with the client's energy field, shifts toward higher vibrations in the form of a healing response become possible. This resonates with the teachings of Florence Nightingale, the founder of modern nursing, who exhorted her students to: "Put the patient in the best possible condition [environment] for nature to act upon him ... for nature alone heals."[11]

Illness has meaning and purpose as part of life's mystery. Allowing for miracles is a core principle of Watson's work because "[the practitioner] is open to the mystery of a deeper order of the universe unfolding within a bigger picture than the human mind."[12] The mysteries of illness, healing, life, and death are beyond our human comprehensions.

The timing of healing is also a mystery. Some heal quickly; others heal slowly or not at all; and still others heal in unanticipated ways. Healing almost never occurs within the confines of medical calendars or dictates.

Each person has the unique task of finding meaning in life. This is an endeavor vividly described in psychiatrist Viktor Frankl's personal story of surviving three years in a Nazi concentration camp where he was able to assign personal meaning to his relationships while enduring harsh slave labor.[13]

Client empowerment comes through education, learning self-care, self-affirmation, and connection to Source. The philosophy of caring guides practitioners to engage in genuine teaching-learning experiences while addressing the whole person. The goal is to empower clients in their personal development and healing. Watson advises the practitioner to be "present to, and supportive of, the expression of positive and negative feelings as a connection with deeper spirit of self and the one-being-cared-for."[14]

Clients need to learn to administer personal self-care rather than continuing to depend on the practitioner for emotional and physical support. The client-practitioner relationship is an evolving dynamic where personal growth is experienced by both. Put another way, each person is enhanced in some way by the nature of a healthy working relationship.

To relate to others positively, there must be a common language, a feeling of mutual respect and a sense of personal connection. HT practitioners apply these principles to help establish trust and safety so that healing can ensue. "Developing and sustaining helping-trusting, authentic caring relationships" occurs through caring moments.[15] A caring moment takes place when the practitioner connects with the soul of another person. Watson explains that "the whole caring-healing-loving consciousness is contained within a single caring moment ... [This] consciousness exists through and transcends time and space and can be dominant over physical dimensions."[16] Additionally, a caring relationship is one "that invites emergence of human spirit, opening to authentic potential, being authentically present, allowing the person to explore options—choosing the best action for self for 'being-in-right-relation' at any given point in time."[17]

In summary, Healing Touch is based on spiritual and scientific principles. Evidence-based knowledge about energy medicine is growing steadily. Concurrently, HT embraces the mystery of healing as new discoveries emerge. Those who are scientifically minded will learn about scientific studies related to energy therapies, consciousness, and intentionality. Those who are interested in spiritual aspects will recognize HT as a contemporary version of the ancient arts of hands-on healing. The HT Program curriculum provides a healthy balance of both perspectives in a professional format.

The Ten-Step Healing Touch Sequence

The Healing Touch Sequence is a structure used to guide the progression of each HT session from beginning to end. This series of steps is based on the nursing process used by holistic healthcare practitioners. Though listed below in linear fashion, the ten steps are not necessarily done in sequence. Depending on preferences, time realities, and settings, the first five steps of the sequence can be modified as long as they are addressed before hands-on administration of HT interventions.

Time spent on each step will vary. For example, HT practitioners in a private practice have the luxury of an hour or more with ample time for intake interviews or updates as well as for client teaching. Practitioners working in hospital settings may only have several minutes for a session, so they must know how to prepare themselves quickly and use most of the time to administer a method.

The ten steps of the Healing Touch sequence are:

1. Client intake or update

2. Practitioner preparation

3. Pretreatment energetic assessment

4. Mutual goal and intention setting

5. Identification of health issues

6. Implementation of one or more treatment interventions

7. Posttreatment energetic assessment

8. Grounding and releasing

9.   Evaluation and feedback

10.   Further planning and growthwork

Each of the ten steps of the session are described in the following text. Students of the program address each of the steps in detail as they study and integrate the core curriculum.

1. Intake or Update

HT practitioners set the safe space for the practitioner-client relationship from the first moment they meet a client. They continue to hold this focus for the duration of their working relationship. Typically, during a first session, an intake interview takes place to discuss client health history, current health concerns, stresses, support systems, experience with energy therapies, and beliefs about healing. This is a holistic interview which touches on the physical, emotional, mental, and spiritual aspects of the recipient. Key points are documented on the intake interview form. (A sample form is given in appendix D.)

Practitioners note the client's use of language, which usually gives clues about the state of energetic health. Comments such as "I'm drained" or "I feel scattered" are indicators of an inner state of depletion. Alternately, comments such as "I'm charged up" or "I feel expanded" reflect an energetic state of positive health. It's also helpful to note correspondence between what the client says, body language, tone of voice, and facial expressions.

Practitioners often use number scales to evaluate change before and after treatments. For example, rating scales may describe levels of pain, range of motion in a joint, or states of anxiety and relaxation. Whereas a nurse may document wound margin measurements, signs of infection, or medication dosages, lay practitioners can assess general ratings of pain, emotional states, or other symptoms. Unless they are licensed physicians, nurses, or other credentialed health caregivers, HT practitioners never diagnose or prescribe, but they assess energy levels, set goals, treat, and educate.

For subsequent sessions, updates of current significant events in the client's life are reviewed. Sometimes clients report a marked improvement, or they may report little change or that new issues have surfaced.

Practitioners are constantly aware of maintaining healthy boundaries while at the same time holding caring intention and compassion for the client. Modern healthcare emphasizes being objective and unemotional with clients. Most practitioners have learned that it is normal, natural, and healthy to feel emotion toward clients, but that it is essential to hold to effective boundaries.

2. Practitioner Preparation

Practitioners always prepare inwardly with centering, grounding, and attuning as conscious energetic steps to serve as instruments of healing. They place themselves in the highest state of consciousness possible. Practitioner preparation is a way of life since one's inner spiritual life resonates with the shared biofield of the client. Practitioner preparation is a conscious return to a centered state of mind before approaching clients. Ideally, this takes place many times throughout the day as an ongoing effort of mindfulness.

3. Pretreatment Energetic Assessment

HT students learn how to use their hands to assess the client's biofield. With repetition, most practitioners learn to use their "hand scans" to discern whether the client's biofield is healthy (buoyant, symmetrical, flowing, warm) or compromised (stagnant, asymmetrical, congested, cold or hot).

HT students also learn to use a pendulum, a small weighted object that can be consciously held over the energy centers to determine their strength and functioning. Compromised chakras can be noted and treated during an intervention and then reevaluated for change. It takes some students a while to learn to trust themselves in assessing and they learn to "get their egos out of the way." Energetic assessment helps practitioners to select the most effective treatment method to use with the client.

4. Mutual Goal and Intention Setting

Practitioners and clients mutually agree on a goal and intention for healing. In addition, they may also identify long-term goals. The goals are stated in positive terms to keep thoughts and visualizations focused on identified outcomes. For example, a goal statement of "I want to quit smoking" would be restated as "I want to find new and healthy ways to manage my stress" or "I want to be smoke-free."

5. Identification of Health Issues

Based on the intake, practitioner and client identify the concerns to be addressed. Practitioners with a medically oriented scope of practice may be able to identify physical conditions and have an understanding of physiology, anatomy, and pathology. Practitioners without medical backgrounds are taught how to assess and treat within their own scope of practice as identified by the HTP Code of Ethics and Scope of Practice Statements (given in appendix B).

6. Healing Touch Intervention(s)

HT interventions follow practitioner preparation, determination of health concerns, mutual goal setting, and completion of the energy assessment. Seasoned practitioners accustomed to working in time-limited situations may sense a client's energies and prepare themselves in several seconds. They can also apply HT as energetic first aid or when a limited amount of time is available.

Students learn which methods are best for certain ailments or conditions, and a number of HT methods are universally applicable. The practitioner may also determine the order for administering methods. Focused intention for the client's highest good is the essential ingredient since the quality of an intervention is vastly more important than quantity.

7. Posttreatment Energetic Assessment

After a sense of completion ensues, the practitioner reassesses the biofield and chakras to determine change. Often, the chakras will be more lively and flowing and the aura will be more balanced and symmetrical. Practitioners document energy treatment outcomes for reference and to help in future planning. As with all healthcare records, documentation is kept confidential and securely stored.

8. Grounding and Releasing

Because the practitioner's and client's energy fields interpenetrate during HT sessions, it's important to recreate separate boundaries at completion. A sense of oneness and compassion is a common experience for both givers and receivers, and this sense of connection can be remembered and treasured. Recreating separate boundaries allows the client to feel empowered with his sense of individuality.

When the practitioner does not consciously conduct a release, there is a possibility that she will take on residue from the client's energy field in the form of temporary symptoms, tiredness, or headaches. If practitioners forget to release adequately after a session, they can consciously do so as soon as they remember.

The facilitator grounds the client at the end of the session by holding the client's feet, ankles, shoulders, or arms. These gestures help clients to return fully into the body. Grounding is essential if the client is proceeding to tasks such as driving or returning to work. Practitioners frequently address clients by name at this time and encourage them to take deep breaths to assist returning to the present. I say the following to my clients slowly and clearly while holding the feet: "[Name of client], bring your attention to your breath. Let each breath bring you back to full, waking consciousness. Bring back with you memory of physical vitality, emotional balance, mental clarity, and alignment with Spirit."

In settings where clients can remain relaxed after treatments, at home or in a healthcare facility, deep relaxation or sleep may ensue. Closure can be effected by simply stating, "We are finished now" or "I'm departing now, please continue to relax into your healing."

9. Evaluation and Feedback

Once the client is grounded, it's helpful to encourage discussion about the experience of the treatment. The vast majority of recipients experience relaxation. Some client reports will match practitioners' perceptions; others may be quite surprising. Recipients may share detailed experiences of dream states, spiritual experiences, color perceptions, conversations with friends or family on the other side, specific body responses, or relief of pain or other symptoms, whereas others will say they just felt relaxed or fell asleep.

Occasionally, some people note an exaggeration of symptoms. This is usually a sign that something has come into awareness that is ready to be released and dissipate. For example, a person with flu may experience a temporary exacerbation of symptoms but may recover more quickly than usual afterward. Being unattached to outcomes is helpful at such times because it is difficult for practitioners to accept the possibility of someone feeling worse after a session. Follow-up contacts are important for both practitioner and client to discuss related issues and perceptions.

The relaxation response is a frequent outcome of HT sessions, and research indicates it is a powerful way for the body to begin healing physically and emotionally.[18] Ideally, clients will learn to initiate their own relaxation and self-care practices.

10. Further Planning and Growthwork

As the session nears its end, the practitioner documents the client's verbal and bodily responses. The last moments are given to developing a plan of care for supporting the momentum of healing set in motion during the session.

Practitioners and clients take time to discuss further self-empowerment with the Self Chakra Connection (described in chapter 13), the Spiral Meditation (chapter 7) or Pain Management techniques (chapter 6). Other plans of care include taking time to support enjoyable activities such as reading books or taking classes. Seeking out other healthcare modalities such as massage therapy, chiropractic care, psychotherapy, or seeing physicians for diagnostic evaluations enhance the treatment plan. With permission, discussion with other healthcare practitioners can be arranged to foster an effective team approach for increasing client wellness. If a client's needs exceed the practitioner's scope of practice, referral is considered to be an ethical requirement.

To conclude, the reader can see how the principles and concepts presented in the ten-step HT sequence lay the groundwork for working therapeutically with clients. However, specific HT techniques are an empty shell without the understanding of professional, ethical, and spiritual foundations described in this book. The next chapters build on what you have already learned and address major contents of the core curriculum starting with Level One, which introduces several methods that can be immediately applied after the first class.

Chapter Notes

1. J. Watson, *Nursing: The philosophy and science of caring*, rev. ed. (Boulder, CO: University Press of Colorado, 2008), 25.

2. *Ibid.*, xviii.

3. *Ibid.*, 144.

4. J. Fitzpatrick and A. Whall, Conceptual Models of *Nursing: Analysis and application* (Saddle River, NJ: Prentice-Hall, 2005), 306.

5. Watson, *op. cit.*, 283.

6. *Ibid.*, 287.

7. *Ibid.*, 31.

8. *Ibid.*, 41.

9. *Ibid.*, 233.

10. Florence Nightingale, quoted in B. M. Dossey, L. Keegan, and C. E. Guzetta (eds.), *Holistic Nursing Handbook for Practice*, fourth ed. (Sudbury, MA: Jones & Bartlett, 2005), 833.

11. Watson, 192.

12. V. E. Frankl, *Man's Search for Meaning* (New York: Washington Square Press, 1963).

14. Watson, 31.

15. *Ibid.*, 81.

16. Fitzpatrick and Whall, *op. cit.*, 312.

17. Watson, 17.

18. Dossey, Keegan, and Guzetta, *op.cit.*, 524.

Chapter 6
Opening the Doors: Level One of the Healing Touch Curriculum

Cynthia Hutchison, DNSc, RN, MSN, HTCP/I

Health is not only to be well,
but to use well every power we have."

—Florence Nightingale, 1893

So far, we discussed the theoretical underpinnings of Healing Touch, its major concepts and the Ten-step Sequence. We're now ready to describe some of the Healing Touch methods. The best place to learn Healing Touch is in a classroom with a certified instructor and an interactive, supportive group of participants. Group energy enhances the experience of giving and receiving HT and a certified instructor provides reflective opportunities to notice differences and similarities in participants' energies. Some of the basics can be learned in other ways, such as reading this book and putting one or several methods into practice.

Magnetic Passes: Hands in Motion and Hands Still

The first method learned in the Level One curriculum is the foundation for learning the subsequent over thirty methods. The hands can direct the facilitator's intention in two basic ways for healing. Either the hands are kept still above a compromised area of the human energy field or they move. All hands-on healing methods stem from these two hand gestures to facilitate multi-dimensional healing.

The most central method in HT is named Magnetic Passes. It is a technique derived from the work of early twentieth century intuitive healer, Alice Bailey.[1] Preparation of the practitioner is essential because simply applying hand gestures will do nothing if they are not accompanied by the practitioner's intention for the highest good of the client, a neutral inner stance without expectations, and the creation of the therapeutic space.

Ideally, practitioners gather information about the client's health concerns and current issues. However, there are times when HT is given to recipients who are unable to communicate such as preverbal children, comatose or highly medicated patients, and persons suffering from dementia or mental disorders. Also, there are situations where HT first aid must be applied since the interventions can be highly effective at the scene of an accident where there is no time or opportunity for data collection.

To bring Magnetic Passes to life, let's imagine a forty-five-year-old client named Jane who experiences mental and emotional stress from her job and financial situation. Jane also recently had knee replacement surgery for an old hockey injury. She continues to have pain in her left knee well after the six-week recovery period which interferes with her work and functioning at home. Jane sets up an appointment with HT practitioner Sara whom she has known for some time.

After intake, Sara assists Jane to get comfortable in a recliner, placing supportive pillows as needed and covering her with a light blanket for warmth. Sara has received informed consent from Jane by explaining the Magnetic Passes technique she will use above the body with possible light touch. Jane relaxes while Sara assesses Jane's biofield and notes areas of depleted, uneven temperature and asymmetry. The left leg and knee feel cold which indicates a compromised pattern in flow of the vital life force.

Sara centered and grounded herself prior to Jane's coming, but she reinforces this awareness and then attunes to Jane's body in preparation for implementing Magnetic Passes.

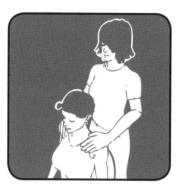

Figure 6.1. Practitioner Attunes to the Client.

Sara gradually and gracefully moves her hands over the length of Jane's body from head to toe in a downward direction. Without any physical touch, her hands continually move in hand-over-hand flowing motions that resemble boat paddles moving through a river. Sara's hands sometimes move slowly, at other times more quickly, and the strokes vary in length. She is "following the energy," remaining aware of what she is sensing as she spends additional time smoothing the field over the left leg until its flow pattern matches the rest of Jane's body.

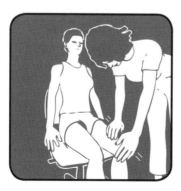

Figure 6.2. Practitioner's Hands in Motion over an Affected Area.

After several minutes, Jane becomes increasingly more relaxed and peaceful. Her response is evidenced by deeper, abdominal breaths, facial "ironing" to a more youthful appearance as muscles relax, improved skin color, and flaccidity in the large muscles of the body.

Magnetic Passes with Hands in Motion is the most basic method in HT to clear congestion or density from the biofield. Using one's imagination, the hand movements described look like cleansing gestures. The practitioner appears to be "sweeping, clearing, moving, unclogging or removing" something, which in this case may be the blocks to energy flow resulting from Jane's surgery and medications. Many clients describe the sense of something being cleared which results in their feeling unburdened, more open, flowing, or balanced.

Sara now proceeds by applying Magnetic Passes with the Hands Still. Aware of Jane's recent surgery and pain, Sara gently places one hand on the left hip and the other on the left ankle with just enough physical contact for Jane to perceive her presence. Sara's intention is enhanced by visualizing warmth and energetic flow in the entire leg. She images the anatomy and physiology of the leg while allowing the energy to modulate as needed for Jane's healing. She holds her hands in this position for several minutes as she notes changes in muscle tension and temperature.

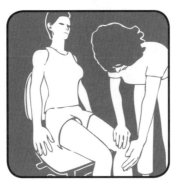

Figure 6.3. Hands Still on the Body.

Whether direct physical touch is used or the hands are in the field above the body, the result is similar. The practitioner continuously discerns which form of touch to use and takes client preferences into consideration.

Next, Sara feels drawn to place her hands directly over the incision area at the knee. She gently holds her hands above area about three inches above the surgical site. As she holds this position, she senses pulsation. The flow continues and then decreases in intensity after a few minutes. These sensations are a sampling of the many varieties of flow patterns Sara learned to identify in her years of practice. She notes that Jane is very relaxed, perhaps asleep.

Sara feels complete with the HT interventions and brings the session to a close. She reassesses Jane's energy system to find that Jane's field now is a consistent warm temperature and is nicely symmetrical. There are no cold or depleted areas.

Sara holds the intention for their two energy fields to separate referred to as "releasing" in HT, and confidently holds Jane's feet in a grounding gesture for a minute to assist her returning to full awareness. She speaks Jane's name and tells her to take several deep breaths.

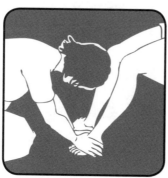

Figure 6.4. Grounding and Releasing Gesture.

After a minute or so, Jane looks up and they share their experiences as part of the evaluation and feedback portion of the sequence. Jane reports significant relaxation, even falling asleep for a short period of time. Her leg pain is reduced from a previous rating of "seven" to a "one." Sara teaches Jane to apply the smoothing hand motions over the painful area for continued self-care.

HT can be practiced either while sitting up or lying down on a recliner, bed or treatment table. The diagrams below show another form of Magnetic Passes while the client is lying down.

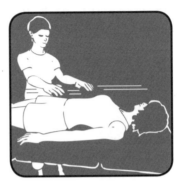

Figure 6.5. Practitioner with Hands in Motion Over Client Lying Down.

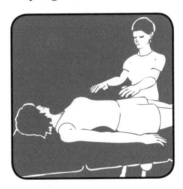

Figure 6.6. Practitioner with Hands Still Above the Client's Body.

Complete, effective treatment can be given with just this method. The practitioner can alternate Hands in Motion and Hands Still and apply both over the entire area of the physical body or over specific areas. In fact, using Magnetic Passes as the entire energy treatment is closely related to methods developed earlier by Dr. Dolores Krieger and Dora Kunz called Therapeutic Touch[2] which was the first hands-on healing method to be introduced in Western medical settings. Other energy therapy training programs use different names to identify similar energetic processes.

Learning to Assess the Energy Body

The basics for assessing a person's energy field and centers are included in the Level One curriculum. This book cannot address or demonstrate energetic assessment in detail, but a short summary describes hand assessment and penduling.

Hand Scan Assessment

When a practitioner is centered and grounded, she "tunes into" the energy of the client while paying attention to hand sensations and her intuition. These skills usually develop over time and are combined with active listening and therapeutic communication.

Practitioners with hand sensitivity notice specific sensations when working with people who have stress or disease. Words often used to describe human energy can be viewed in table 6.1. The table also includes words that describe auditory and visual energetic cues which some practitioners are able to discern. Many HT students learn to scan the body with the hands close to the client's body initially and then advance to the other levels of the field that extend beyond the body.

Movement	Temperature Differences	Energetic Disruptions	
Dense	Hot	Void	Bumpy
Congested	Warm	Empty	Irregular
Heavy	Burning	Drained	Off Center
Flowing	Cool	Hole	Painful
Active	Cold	Blocked	Sharp
Activated	Icy	Stuck	Jagged
Vibrating		Tear	Stinging
Pulsating		Ripped	Prickley
Pulling		Leak	Sticky
Pushing		Bulging	Shaky

Sensations		Visual Perceptions	Auditory Perceptions
Electric	Hard	Colors	Words
Tingling	Structured	Lights	Phrases
Buzzing	Stiff	Images	Sentences
Magnetic	Shielded	Symbols	Tones
Vital	Armored	Thought Forms	Sounds
Full	Sweaty	People / Guides	Voices
Bubbly	Wet	Light	
Bouncy	Slippery	Brilliant	
Expansive	Clammy	Luminous	
Fuzzy		Dark	
		Muddy	

Table 6.1. Descriptors of client energy as sensed by practitioners.

Using a Pendulum

The use of a pendulum, a well-known form of the ancient art of dowsing, is another assessment tool for HT practitioners. Pendulums are especially useful for practitioners who have limited hand sensitivity for discerning energy field disruptions. A centered and grounded practitioner can receive helpful information about the flow patterns in the energy centers and to discern which body areas require treatment.

In general, HT practitioners are taught that a clockwise pendulum motion over a specific chakra indicate a healthy, functional energy center. Any other movement, such as counterclockwise, horizontal, vertical, diagonal, elliptical, chaotic or lack of movement is considered indicative of compromised, less than optimal function. While beginners to energy modalities sometimes feel discouraged about not mastering hand scanning and penduling during Level One, these skills develop with practice.

Magnetic Clearing

Magnetic Clearing is a full body method described by Janet Mentgen for the purpose of clearing the energy field of congested energy. It is a variation of Magnetic Passes. The field is cleared in a systematic way with hands in motion , from above the head to past the feet for 20-30 times or until it feels smooth and balanced. This technique also assists in releasing emotional debris such as feelings of fear, anger, worry and tension. It can be administered by one or two practitioners and can be used by itself or in combination with other HT techniques.

Magnetic Clearing is recommended for the following kinds of individuals:

- clients with a history of prescription or recreational drug use
- patients needing post-operative clearing of anesthesia

- persons suffering chronic pain

- survivors of trauma

- people exposed to environmental toxins

- those with a history of smoking, even after cessation of the habit

- patients with systemic disease or sleep disturbance

- people receiving kidney dialysis

- patients receiving chemotherapy or radiation

The intention behind Magnetic Clearing is to clear the entire biofield of energetic debris, or congestion, which no longer serves the person. Because the biofield exists beyond the physical body, the practitioner begins long lengthwise clearing gestures from about approximately eighteen inches above the client's head to below the feet. The client can be sitting or reclining. The practitioner's fingers are relaxed and slightly curled as they are placed well above the head at the beginning of each round of clearing. Going very slowly, so that each round takes about thirty seconds from above the head to past the feet, the practitioner keeps her fingers pointed toward the client's core while simultaneously moving downward. No physical touch is used in this method.

The practitioner repeats this motion until the field feels clear and "smooth as glass." Practitioners often note a sensation of built-up energy in their hands as they move toward the lower body, which usually dissipates after going past the client's feet. Current understandings from quantum mechanics hold that subtle energy is neither created nor destroyed, but rather transformed. In Magnetic Clearing, the practitioner sets intention for congestion to be released from the client's system and transformed into useful or neutral energy as it exits.

Chakra Connection

The Chakra Connection is a full-body balancing technique, first described by physician Brugh Joy[3] and used with permission in HT. It facilitates movement of energy from chakra to chakra, from the lower body to the upper body to energize the whole energy system. The lower body and chakras consist of the legs and the three lower chakras, root, sacral and solar plexus centers while the upper body includes the arms and the three upper chakras, the throat, brow and crown. The heart is the middle chakra and is therefore is seen as the bridge between the upper and lower bodies. The method may be used by itself or in combination with other HT techniques. Its effect for most clients is to feel more energized.

Hand positions are held over each chakra for approximately one minute or until the practitioner senses increased balance, fullness, or an increased flow of vibrancy. Comfortable and stable body mechanics should be maintained so the practitioner can more naturally serve as the conduit for energy. If the practitioner prefers not to touch specific energy centers, the practitioner may visualize and sense the connection with each center through intention while holding hands above the body.

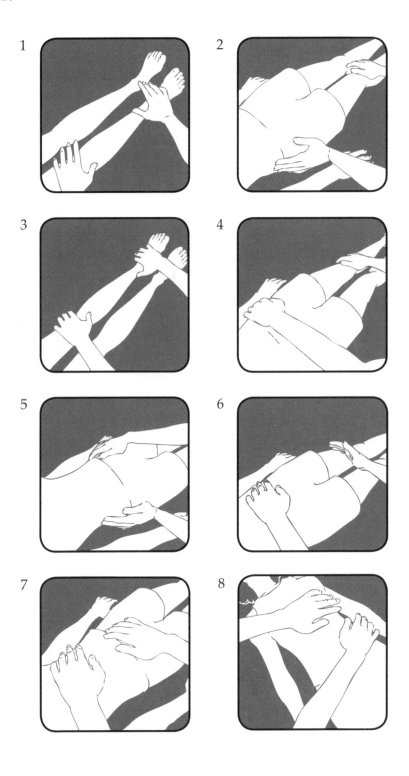

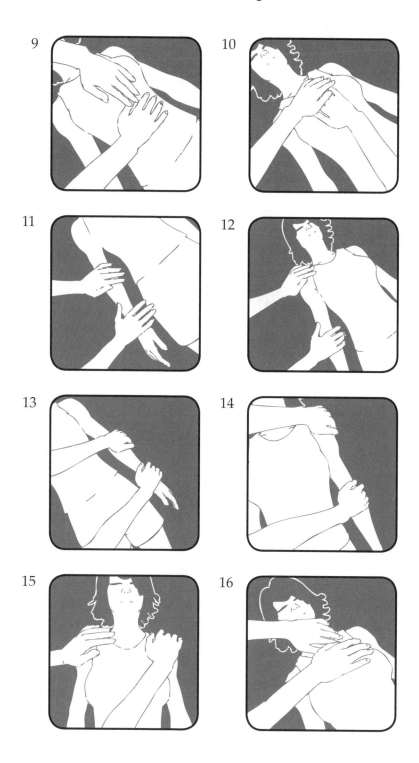

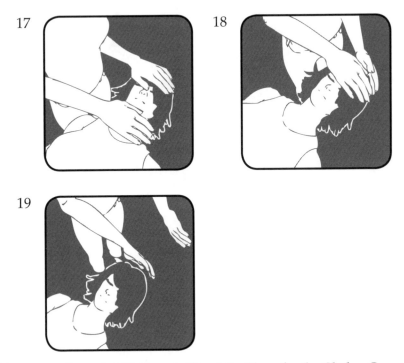

Figures 6.7 through 6.25. Sample Hand Positions for the Chakra Connection.

HT Methods for Headaches and Pain Relief

There are several methods for pain management in HT. Full-body techniques such as the Chakra Connection can be used in combination with local techniques such as Laser and Ultrasound which are described below. Reduction or elimination of pain is commonly reported by those receiving HT and the effects may be temporary or permanent. If more pain relief is needed, the client can administer these methods as a form of self-care which is effective and self-empowering.

Ultrasound

Ultrasound is a focus of light energy directed from the palm chakra through the thumb and two fingers which are held together while moving the fingers repeatedly over the area of the body that is imbalanced. This method breaks up congestion and blocks in the energy field and may be used for arthritic joints, to seal lacerations, to accelerate wound or bone healing, and to relieve constipation or respiratory congestion. It may be used for local aches and pains such as earaches, toothaches and sinus headaches. The practitioner applies Ultrasound for a few minutes, usually followed by Magnetic Passes with Hands in Motion to clear away any congestion. Ultrasound may be repeated as needed.

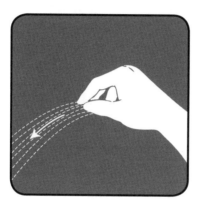

Figure 6.26. Model of Energetic "Ultrasound."

Laser

Laser is similar to Ultrasound in that it is a penetrating focus of light energy extending from one or more fingers pointed toward an imbalanced area. With this method practitioners can work on a very small area deep inside the body where a beam of light could reach. Laser may be applied with still or moving fingers that follow a pathway of the body such as a nerve track to relieve pain or over scar tissue to release its density. Applying laser for a few seconds or up to a minute often provides relief or improvement in symptoms. It may be repeated as needed and taught to clients for self-administration. As with Ultrasound, following up with Magnetic Passes is helpful.

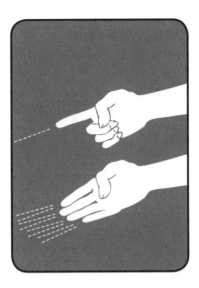

Figure 6.27. Model of Energetic "Laser."

Other Pain Relief Methods

Other local pain relief methods are taught in Level One including the Pain Drain, Sealing a Wound and working with a Pain Ridge or Spike. Each are further variations of Magnetic Passes: Hands in Motion or Hands Still with specific applications for pain.

Headache Relief Techniques

Headaches are commonly experienced events that respond well to HT interventions. The practitioner should first determine the type of headache to be treated as methods will differ. Combining headache treatments with a full-body method helps to restore overall balance, but these local methods can also be used by themselves. Intake when working on a person with a headache includes description of the headache, its duration and intensity, and what has worked in the past.

Tension Headaches

After applying Magnetic Passes: Hands in Motion around the head, the practitioner can follow with Hands Still over the top three chakras starting with the throat and brow and then the brow and crown. Mind Clearing (see Chapter 7), Magnetic Clearing and Chakra Connection are also known to be effective. Anything that can be done to elicit the relaxation response will benefit persons with tension headaches. This includes peaceful music, massage, use of positive imagery, affirmations and taking time to rest.

Sinus Headaches

The practitioner alternates Ultrasound over the client's congested or painful sinus areas with Magnetic Passes: Hands in Motion. The client should remain in an upright position to decrease head tension and allow for drainage of sinus fluids once the Ultrasound method begins to break up congestion. Keep tissues handy because this technique often brings immediate results!

Migraine Headaches

Migraine headaches can be helped with Magnetic Passes - Hands in Motion starting from a distance since the most intense migraine pain may extend far beyond the client's head in the form of an energetic spike. The practitioner attempts to find its point with a hand scan and feedback from the client to determine the place for beginning the application of Hands in Motion. She then works gradually to bring the moving hands closer to the patient's head as the energy clears. Once the client is comfortable with the caregiver's hands close to his head, Hands Still may follow to modulate energy and seal the area.

Migraine headaches are often cyclical and repetitious with debilitating effects that may last two or three days requiring cancellation of life activities. Some who have migraines experience nausea, blackouts or extreme sensitivity to noise or light. HT practitioners frequently need 15 minutes or more to facilitate relief. The client's healing process can be supported with repeated HT treatments during and in between exacerbations and with improved self- care. Consultation with other holistic health care practitioners can enhance the team approach to assisting the client.

The Chakra Spread

Janet Mentgen adapted this method from a hospice nurse who used energy medicine practices. She identified this method as one which could be helpful for someone who is dying as well as for anyone experiencing a significant life transition. This method seems to open the chakras and blend them through the field in such a way that deep healing can occur.

The Chakra Spread is done slowly and gently with a client who is lying down or reclining comfortably. Initially, the practitioner takes a minute or so to hold each of the client's hands and feet, one at a time, as a way of setting the intention for each of the endpoints to allow congestion to exit. The method consists of moving over all of the major energy centers and legs, starting from two or more feet above the crown of the head, to gently spread apart the chakra to assist its full opening and releasing. The practitioner's hands are consciously placed within the vortex of each chakra before slowly moving the hands apart, horizontal to the body, and bringing them beyond the outer borders of the energy field. Each center is thus "spread" three times in the following order: crown, brow, throat, heart, solar plexus, sacral, root, knees, and ankles. The hands move slowly from the energy center to the outermost imagined level of the personal energy field to release the patient's energy to the Universal Energy Field.

Then, the cycle of moving through the centers from the crown to the feet is repeated two more times in exactly the same way. The practitioner may note changes in the field and chakras with each pass. Often a deep relaxation response is noted as the client consciously or unconsciously receives the meditation.

The final gesture of the Chakra Spread includes physical touch as the practitioner holds one of the client's hands with one hand and places his other hand over the client's heart. This final caring position is held until the practitioner feels a sense of completion. In the case of bedridden patients, continuing to sleep or rest effects the best closure.

In summary, this chapter provided a brief overview of some of the central methods contained in the Level One HT Program curriculum. As taught in the weekend workshops, the course material provides a solid foundation for beginning practice in using energy medicine concepts. The methods facilitate body-mind-spirit healing in oneself and others. Students, whether they are healthcare professionals or interested laypersons, have received the theoretical, ethical, and essential background that provides them with enough experience and knowledge to begin integration of the ideas into their everyday lives.

Chapter Notes

1. A. Bailey, *Esoteric Healing: A treatise on the seven rays* (New York: Lucis Publishing Company, 1953).

2. B. Joy, *Joy's Way: A map for the transformational journey* (New York: J.P. Tarcher,1979) 191-196.

3. D. Krieger, (1993) *Accepting Your Power to Heal: The personal practice of Therapeutic Touch* (Santa Fe, NM: Bear & Co., 1993).

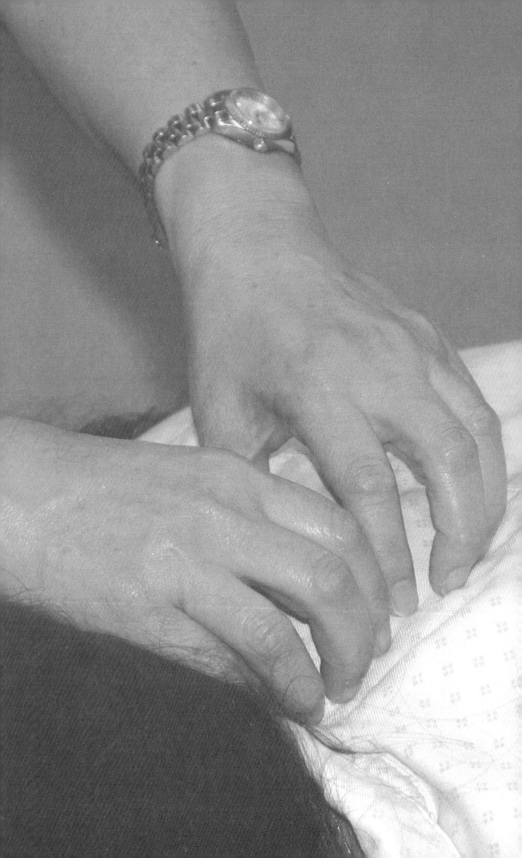

Chapter 7
Increased Integration of Practice at Level Two

Cynthia Hutchison, DNSc, RN, MSN, HTCP/I

The heart is the hub of all holy places. Go there and roam in it.
—Bhagavan Nityananda

After taking Level One, many students follow their sense of connection to the Healing Touch learning curriculum by signing up for the next class. However, healthy skepticism is also encouraged. Instructors ask students to check out their own perceptions of the methods and to practice them in safe, appropriate settings. The decision to continue with the training program often comes after learners have a direct hands-on experience, an "ah-ha" moment when it all begins to make sense. Here's a story from Peg Olson, a nurse who had the opportunity to immediately use her Level One learning to relieve "phantom limb" sensations.

Peg's Story

I decided to complete my bachelor's program after twenty years in nursing and attended HT Level One class as part of my independent study. Still a full-blown skeptic about the methods, I returned Monday morning with an urgent call from Gladys, one of my elderly medical patients with diabetes.

While I was out of town, she had to have a leg amputation as gangrene had set in due to complications. Gladys was very alert and knew about phantom limb pain which can often follow an amputation. She asked me to use HT because she was convinced it would help her. I hesitated, tried to do everything just right, reread my notes and prevaricated, but Gladys insisted, "Peg, just do it!"

I centered myself and asked for guidance and for Gladys' highest good. I moved my hands over her body with Magnetic Passes until I felt a cold place. Gladys exclaimed, "Oh, that feels so good!"

I stopped and looked at my hands—they were over the empty place where her leg would have been. Gladys described a cool, soothing sensation and stated her foot and leg now felt properly aligned. Then, she had the first bowel movement after seven days of struggling with digestive blockage.

I was so shocked and surprised! I had to accept that "this stuff really works" and went on to take Level Two. All this was many years ago but it is still with me like it just happened. I give thanks to the Universe for this immediate lesson because otherwise I might have walked away from HT.

****

The students who go on to Level Two usually have several insightful and surprising experiences as they practice the methods, although they might not be as dramatic as the one described. Students delight in sharing their experiences with a new class. Hearing each others' descriptions of HT's impact of HT on their lives further validates experiences and sets the tone for continued learning.

As they resonate with the concepts, principles, and practices of Healing Touch, students find themselves gaining deeper comprehension. The foundation for heart-centered energy healing sessions is laid out in the first course but Level Two continues by offering the following learning opportunities:

- Developing data collection and assessment skills in order to administer and document a comprehensive, holistically-oriented intake interview

- Adapting the ten-step HT sequence for specific client health issues, including integration of several new HT methods

- Documenting HT sessions

- Addressing back and neck issues

- Learning Mind Clearing, Spiral Meditation and other full body and local methods

- Increased comprehension of the HTP Code of Ethics and Scope of Practice Statements.

The Intake Interview

No matter how well a student may have memorized or intellectualized techniques, sequences or concepts, unless the sacred space is consciously created, little or nothing is likely to occur in the form of healing in clients. Dr. Janet Quinn, a highly respected holistic nurse whose background includes teaching caring science, Therapeutic Touch research, and spiritually-oriented consultation, goes to the core of Healing Touch practice when she describes the creation of safe, therapeutic space. She recommends that practitioners ask themselves, "If I *am* the [healing] environment… for this client, how can I *be* a more healing environment? How can I become a safe space, a sacred healing vessel for this client in this moment? In what ways can I look into this person to draw out healing? How can I use my consciousness, my being, my voice, my touch, my face, for healing?"[1]

No practitioner creates healing. Instead, the practitioner's role is to facilitate a peaceful environment so that healing can occur at whatever level is possible for the individual. This also means that practitioners know how to use themselves as therapeutic agents who give unconditional love to the best of their abilities.

By holding the intention for the highest good of each client during a session and focusing on the intention behind specific interventions, practitioners find numerous client responses ranging from welcome relaxation to remarkable outcomes and insights. It is impossible to predict what client responses will be, but HT practitioners learn to expect the unexpected along with improvements in clients' body-mind-spirit health. As mentioned in the previous chapter, nonattachment to specific outcomes is a required stance.

It is not unusual for the intake interview, first in the ten-step HT sequence, to begin the healing process. Practitioners center, ground and attune themselves prior to the interview so that clients can feel comfortable sharing information about themselves and their health concerns. Practitioners learn to utilize whatever time is available. The inwardly-prepared practitioner uses the client's information to know the best way to work with the person at a particular moment in time.

When clients feel they are accepted without judgment by the helper, they can explore their lives more fully. Being heard without interruption can be enlightening since clients will often "connect the dots" and make sense of the significant patterns in their lives.

Beyond basic demographic data, practitioners ask about the client's experiences with energy medicine and answer questions about HT. Knowing the caregiver's approach helps to put clients at ease. Other intake items include the client's current health issues and relevant healthcare professionals (both mainstream and holistic practitioners), the health history including medications and lifestyle patterns. The caregiver helps clients to explore emotional stressors such as illness, work, relationships, finances, and losses as well as current social supports and self-care practices. Clients are also asked about perceived causes of their current health issues and ways spiritual beliefs influence their lives.

Some people trust more easily than others. HT practitioners allow trust to build and never push clients for personal information. They know that natural development of relationship occurs over time. Clients with a history of trauma may inwardly long for opportunities to trust other human beings, yet this aspect of healing cannot be rushed or forced.

In addition to learning about energetically-oriented intake interviews and documenting them according to professional standards, students learn a number of new HT interventions.

Spiral Meditation Technique

The Spiral Meditation, which was incorporated into the HTP curriculum with Brugh Joy's permission, can be used to connect the major and minor chakras in a single spiral pattern.[2] This method reflects a sacred geometry pattern that energetically supports the opening and expansion of the energy system for increased functioning. It may be used at the beginning of a session with the intention of setting the stage for deep healing with other HT methods or by itself to let the client experience a state of energetic expansion within a safe environment.

To begin, the practitioner places her hand over the heart of the client, the central chakra of the seven major chakras (described in chapter 2). Experiencing the client's heart center as a place where the divine spark of life energetically resides, the practitioner visualizes a source of light energy gradually spiraling outward in a clockwise fashion from the heart center to the other centers in a specific pattern with ever widening arcs of movement. Each position is usually held about a minute or until the practitioner senses readiness to move on to the next position. Following the intention for connecting, balancing and expanding each of the client's chakras, the practitioner moves from the heart to the solar plexus, then on to the high heart, the spleen, sacral area, throat, root, brow, knees, crown, ankles, and transpersonal point above the head. The movements reflect opening of the field by using an ever-increasing spiral arc pattern which ends at the transpersonal point also known as the point of individuation. The client's field is usually expanded fully and the client has moved into a state of relaxed receptivity.

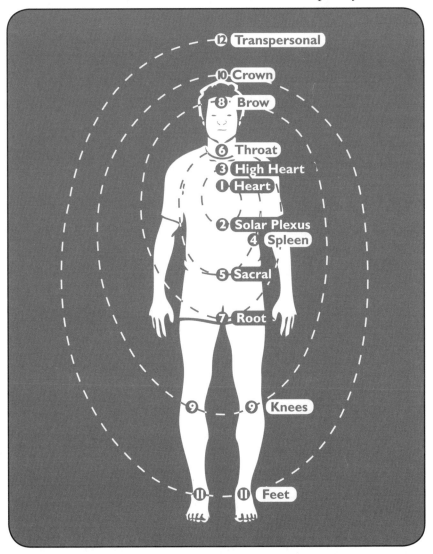

Figure 7.1. Spiral Meditation Technique Pattern.

Toward the end of the session, the practitioner completes the intervention by closing the spiral in a counterclockwise direction, starting with the transpersonal point and gradually moving through the pattern back toward the heart. The reverse of the spiral differs in that the time taken is shorter and the intention is to bring the field back to its more normal energetic boundaries. Full grounding usually occurs by the time the practitioner reaches the endpoint, the heart center. Though the spiral has been closed, the chakras remain open, leaving the client in enhanced self-awareness and internal balance. This method may also be taught as a self-healing technique the client can use as needed.

Healing Touch Back and Neck Techniques

The uniquely upright posture of *homo sapiens* frequently leads to back problems and pain. The HT curriculum includes techniques to assist relief for back and neck issues. Practitioners are encouraged to employ the Chakra Connection first in order to prepare the client's body since overall relaxation facilitates working energetically with the back.

After receiving the Chakra Connection on the front of the body, the client turns over and relaxes face down on a treatment table. Practitioners assess the back area with a visual scan to perceive if the back and legs are in alignment and scan the back with their hands and/or a pendulum. The practitioner notes and documents perceived misalignments of the numerous vertebral chakras. Then, an abbreviated version of the Chakra Connection is given to deepen the connection of the feet to the legs and across to the hips to align the lower body.

A basic technique follows described as **Opening Spinal Energy Flow** in which the practitioner places his palms or fingers on or above the base of the spine and the top of the neck to enhance spinal energy flow. This position is held a minute or longer or until a sense of flow is established.

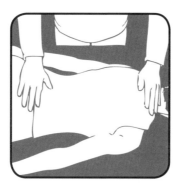

Figure 7.2. Opening Spinal Energy Flow.

In order to create relaxation for the complicated musculature of the matrix of muscles surrounding the spinal vertebrae, the **Vertebral Spiral Technique** is applied. This method entails applying small circular movements immediately next to both sides of the spiny processes of the back. The circular movements can be done either above the body or with light touch. Clockwise circular motions using "ultrasound fingers" are applied to the right side of the spine while counterclockwise circular movements are applied to the left side. The circular motion is applied ten or more times for each area as a way of clearing out energetic blockage that may be causing congestion, tightness, pain or misalignment. As the practitioner completes the series of circles in each area, she consciously brings her hands upward and outward past the outer level of the client's individual energy field, thus releasing congestion or "that which no longer serves" to free client's energy in that area.

Starting at the base of the neck, the practitioner applies these circular movements to each side of the spine and moves down gradually until the entire spine down to the sacral area has received the intervention.

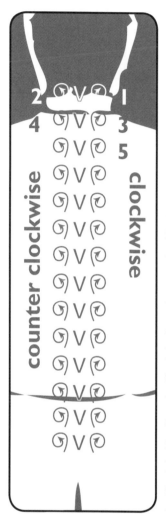

Figure 7.3. Vertebral Spiral Technique.

Most often, the Vertebral Spiral Technique assists in relaxation of the layers of muscles surrounding the spine which are required for staying upright. The practitioner reassesses the back after using the method to see if the spinal chakras have become more balanced and aligned. Vertebrae that remain compromised will hopefully respond to the intervention described next.

The **Hopi Back Technique** was developed by Rudy Noel, a Denver-based healer of Hopi descent, who worked and studied with Janet Mentgen for a number of years. This method seems to work beyond the musculature of the spine and into the nervous system and energetic structures. The four- step process includes applying penetrating "rays of laser light" from the practitioner's fingers on both sides of the spine for a minute or longer into the compromised spinal area. The practitioner simultaneously holds the intention of dissolving blocked energy. This is followed by a similar hand gesture, also on either side of the spine to help draw up the congested energy temporarily into the practitioner's hands to be readied for release from the client's system. The third step is to draw out energetic blockage or congestions by pulling up and away to the far edges of the client's field to be released into the Universal Energy Field. This drawing out motion is done in conjunction with and intentional exhalation from the practitioner or both practitioner and client to enhance the release. The final step of the Hopi Back Technique is to energetically seal the area immediately following the release by having the practitioner place her palms on the area for a minute or more. The Hopi Back Technique may be applied to multiple areas of the back and may be repeated in subsequent HT sessions as needed.

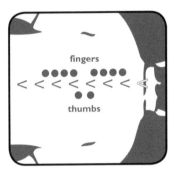

Figure 7.4. Hopi Back Technique Hand Positions.

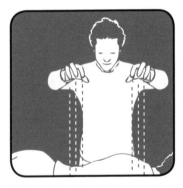

Figure 7.5. Drawing Out Congested Material.

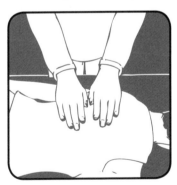

Figure 7.6. Energetically Resealing the Biofield.

While working on a client's back, the practitioner can also apply other local HT methods, such as Ultrasound or Laser for nerve track pain, muscle repair or improved energy circulation. Magnetic Passes: Hands in Motion or Hands Still can also help. Work with the back is completed by holding one hand at each end of the spine (as in diagram 7.2), this time with the intention of bringing the work to closure with improved strength, flow, relaxation and alignment. Clients may report immediate relief or gradual improvement that may continue as the energetic momentum set in motion continues over the next few days.

Treatment of the neck is done with exactly the same methods as for the back. If there is increased sensitivity in the smaller neck musculature from injury or illness, the practitioner needs to use a finer, lighter touch.

Chakra Connection with Body-Centered Interview

The Chakra Connection with Body-Centered Interview, is a type of interview that blends the Chakra Connection with a verbal exploration of events and emotions that relate to specific body memories. The synergy of combining touch to a specific area of the body while inquiring about related traumatic events can empower conscious associations between current symptoms and overall life patterns. When clients see patterns and their possible causes, they can make positive changes. This method also helps the practitioner to clearly see connections between the client's symptoms, her health condition, and energetic patterns.

Mind Clearing

In the time-honored method of learning from each other, Mind Clearing was shared with Janet Mentgen by Rudy Noel who in turn learned it from his studies with healer-author Rosalyn Bruyere.[3] This adapted technique is applied to the head area but brings systemic effects. Mind Clearing is useful for relieving stress, headaches, hypertension, temporal-mandibular joint (TMJ) problems, and emotional distress. It also facilitates a sense of mental clarity and integration between the right and left brain hemispheres. Each position is held for a minute or longer, until the practitioner feels a sense of balance, increased energy flow or a sense of completion. This intervention may be received lying down or sitting up, in conjunction with other methods or by itself.

The practitioner images her energetic fingers gently extending into the client's head, neck and brain, to enhance energetic flow and facilitate a sense of openness and connection. Light physical touch is used in the set of several gestures, and Mind Clearing could be considered a variation of both Magnetic Passes: Hands Still and Hands in Motion.

Figure 7.7. Attuning to the Client with Fingers on the Collarbone.

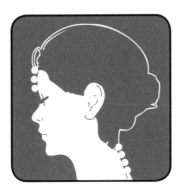

Figure 7.8. Touch to Forehead and Back of Neck.

Figure 7.9. Holding the Occipital Ridge with Neck Stretch.

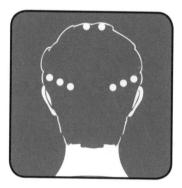

Figure 7.10. Thumbs and Fingers Used to Form a Skullcap.

Figure 7.11. Touch on Both Sides of Pulse above the Ears.

Figure 7.12. Touch to Forehead with Fingertips of Both Hands.

Figure 7.13. Circular Movement Over Temporal Mandibular Joints (TMJ).

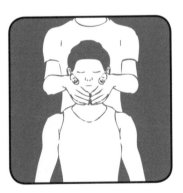

Figure7.14. Lightly Holding Jaws.

The Level Two course curriculum in the Healing Touch Program brings the student from an introductory level of practice to an understanding of the deeper elements of assessment and treatment. Integrating professional practice and HT interventions into full-length sessions provides more tools in the healing art and science of this noninvasive form of energy medicine.

Chapter Notes

1. J. Quinn, "Holding Sacred Space: the nurse as healing environment" (*Holistic Nursing Practice*, 6(4), 1992) 26-35.

2. B. Joy, *Joy's Way: A map for the transformational journey* (New York: Tarcher, 1979).

3. R. Bruyere, *Wheels of Light: A study of the chakras*, (Sierra Madre, CA: Bon Productions, 1989).

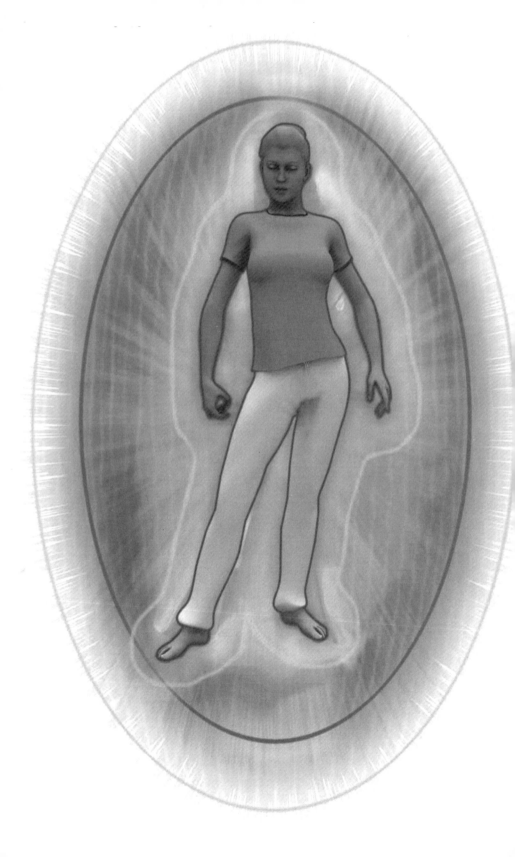

Chapter 8
Multidimensional Approaches at Level Three

Cynthia Hutchison, DNSc, RN, MSN, HTCP/I

That which is real cannot be threatened. That which is not real does not exist. Therein lies divine Peace.

- Author unknown

The content and practice of Level Three takes students to new dimensions of understanding the human energy system. These expanded ways of experiencing energy anatomy are not only fascinating intellectually but inspire awe and wonder about the magnificent creations we are as human beings. The theoretical framework presented by Barbara Brennan in both Hands of Light[1] and Light Emerging[2] is used to introduce the dimensions of energetic anatomy. Learners' imaginations are stretched as they explore the reality of the "hara line" and the "core star." Both these terms are used by Barbara Brennan and have been described in different words by many authors, healers, and spiritual scientists in ancient and contemporary spiritual texts.

The Level Three HT curriculum introduces a full body healing sequence that highlights *chelation,* or "spinning out," and methods that help the practitioner to raise her vibrational frequency. It also integrates comprehension of the multidimensional human energy field. Other methods taught in Level Three include Etheric Template Clearing, and Lymphatic Drainage, methods adapted and developed by Janet Mentgen.

Spiritual Concepts in Healing Touch

Concepts and principles underlying advanced teachings of HT have a strong spiritual basis, but they are presented in a universal way so that everyone who believes in a Creator or Higher Power can personally translate them into their own ideology. Spiritual principles used in HT are addressed in a generic way in order to hold universal appeal and no specific religious or spiritual belief is taught or promoted in HT. Participants are invited to consider their own ideologies as they find resonance with the Healing Touch Program. The belief that conscious, intentional and compassionate touch can positively influence the healing of another person is shared by all who practice HT.

Incorporation of Multiple Dimensions of the Human Being into Healing Touch Treatments

Students of Level Three expand their knowledge of the multidimensional human energy field which includes the chakras and energy field (as described in chapter 2) with additional recognition of the Core Star and the Hara Line. Let's begin with a succinct description of these two aspects and describe how they are adapted in more artful HT sessions.

The Core Star

"Core star" is a term that describes the essential aspect of the Self (note the use of capital "S" to emphasize higher aspects of one's self). The core star represents the divine and eternal aspect of the human being. It is the part of each person that was, is, and will always be whole, healthy, and complete. It exemplifies the purely spiritual essence of the

Self that, when forgotten, may lead people to feel incomplete, unloved or cynical. People who have belief or hope in the eternal spirit Self are often able to endure hardships and maintain courage when life is challenging because of their ability to sense a connection with their deeper capacities that extend beyond the constrictions of the material world.

While the core star is not physical in nature, it can be most easily sensed as somewhere near the waist level of the body between the solar plexus and sacral centers. Energetically, it radiates out from the center of the physical body through the levels of the biofield like a radiant star, hence the name core star. The core star is incorporated into HT practice as students become aware of their multidimensional patterns and learn to consciously expand their core star awareness through each level of the auric field. Self-healing and a sense of personal presence come from this awareness and lift practitioners to a higher vibrational frequency to facilitate entrainment with the client. The practitioner's attunement to the core star essence helps her to remember her wholeness and to better serve as a vessel for others' healing. The client's core star is always aligned with his divine and inherently healthy, whole nature.

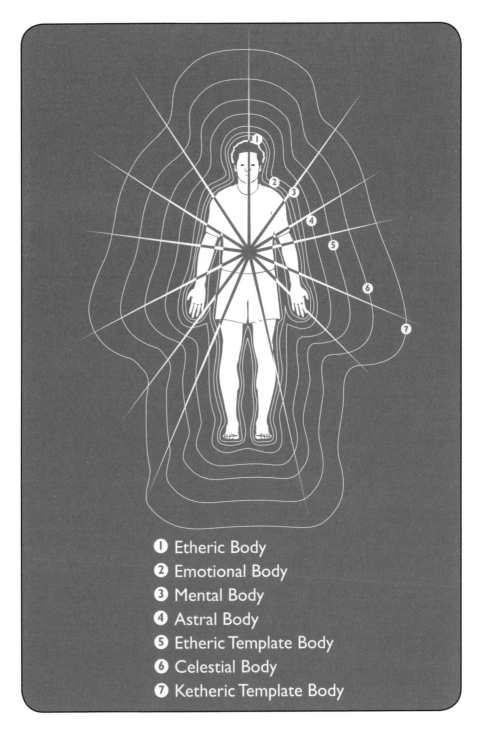

Figure 8.1. Schematic Depiction of the Core Star.

The Hara Line

The hara line can be thought of as the part of the Self that holds the intention for each person's specific lifetime. Intentional alignment with the hara line supports evolution to higher levels of spiritual maturity and expression of the soul's purpose. It also effects the universal intention of caring from the Creator whose qualities are expressed through beauty, truth and goodness. The point above the head, the heart area, and the *tan tien* just below the navel can be thought of as the physically-grounded spiritual locations of thinking, feeling, and willing. The Hara Line thus exemplifies a person's alignment of thought, desires, and action. Human aspirations to be in alignment with the Will of Higher Power are an example of this grounded intention and may be expressed in words such as, "Thy will be done."

The end points of the hara line extend above and below the person from the cosmos to the core of the earth, thus connecting each person simultaneously to heaven and earth. The hara line is a laser-like column of light which holds a vibrational tone that maintains the spirit in physical form to experience life on earth. As stated by Brennan, " It is this one note [one's individual hara line] that holds your body in physical manifestation... This note is the sound the center of the earth makes."[3]

People who seek to be more conscious and moral develop heart-centered compassion and their actions reflect altruism, service to others, and an ethic of caring. For practitioners, experiencing alignment with the hara line enhances self- knowledge and clear thinking.

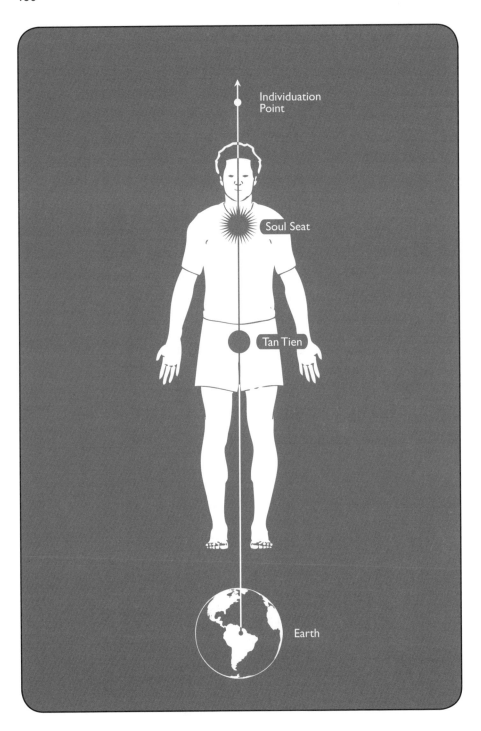

Figure 8.2. Major Aspects of the Hara Line.

The Hara Alignment Meditation is used by practitioners as a self-care, self-healing method and for preparation prior to offering interventions such as chelation methods for the first four layers of the biofield. In the meditation, the practitioner brings awareness to the points on her own hara line to assure that she is aligned with higher will and purpose. The soul aspects of thinking, feeling and willing are consciously aligned with the divine during the Hara Alignment Meditation. The *tan tien* is focused on first to enhance groundedness, physical balance, and self-discipline. It may be experienced by some as a glowing sphere in the belly. It is then imaged to be connected to the center of the earth for grounding to the body, the earth, and the present moment with one's will. Then, the practitioner consciously connects this column of light to the mid-chest area to sense her heart's and soul's desires. The soul seat is activated within the chest area while focusing on one's longing for love and healing in this lifetime. Extending the column of light upward, the individuation point is then sensed above the head as the direct connection to Truth and clear thinking. The hara line is sensed as a continual column of light that firmly connects and aligns the individual to both heaven and earth.

After the hara line is imaged, the practitioner consciously expands the chakras in sequential order from root to crown to assure that they are fully open and flowing. Then, the practitioner senses the core star from the center of the physical self outward through all seven layers or aspects of the auric field. When this meditation of sensing personal multidimensionality is completed, students move on to practice the HT interventions offered in Level Three.

Methods Taught in Level Three

Energetic Chelation

Using the ten-step HT Sequence, practitioners begin with the intake/update, health issues to be addressed, intentions for healing and pre-treatment energetic assessments of the chakras and field. They proceed with the Hara Alignment and move into the hands-on chelation treatment. The hand positions for chelation are similar to those of the Chakra Connection. The consciousness and inner stance of the practitioners is, however, quite different. At this stage of learning, participants are aware the multidimensional nature of the client's field and have greatly expanded their own self-understanding. The intention is to reach all levels of the client's energetic being to facilitate vitality and movement toward greater health.

Energetic chelation, also known as clearing or spinning out, of the first four levels of the auric field (etheric, emotional, mental, astral) can be the first part of a healing sequence. From there, practitioners work with the fifth, sixth and seventh auric levels as needed. Chelating is akin to a powerful energetic cleansing that may also help to balance and energize the client's field.

To learn energetic chelation, students are taught how to spin or open their chakras through visualization and by making actual clockwise pelvic rotations to vitalize their energies. Most practitioners quickly learn how to make their physical movements subtle so the spin resembles the "hum" of a spinning top toy which is rotating quickly. Each practitioner learns how to maintain these high energy vibrations during healing sessions. As practitioners help to cleanse client fields, they also chelate themselves, a joyful reminder of the reciprocal benefits of facilitating work with others and effecting self-care.

Spinal Cleansing

Generally, the spine is cleared during the chelation process, however, if the client has back or spinal issues, additional attention may be helpful. This method can be thought of as a variation of Magnetic Passes: Hands in Motion. The practitioner visualizes and holds the intention for clearing while implementing these hand gestures. The physical steps for Spinal Cleansing include:

1. Making circles with the thumbs starting over the sacral bone areas to loosen congested energy

2. Moving with small circular gestures upward on either side of the spine to the neck area, ending the gesture with a sweep off the top of the head

3. Making larger clockwise circles from the sacral area upward and beyond the head.

Additional Deep Cleansing Treatments

Three other hand positions may be added to assist particular areas of the body in need of further clearing or energizing. They are modifications of both Hands Still and Hands in Motion. The basic concepts of these methods can be understood through the diagrams offered here:

Figure 8.3 "Sandwich" Position of Hands to Modulate Energy Flow.

Figure 8.4. "Cone" Position of Hands to Focus on a Specific Area.

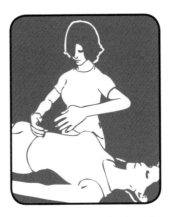

Figure 8.5. "Scooping" as Method of Releasing Congestion.

Etheric Template Clearing

The Etheric Template is the name given to the fifth layer of the human energy field that appears to be a blueprint for the physical body at a more subtle energetic level. Janet Mentgen learned the method she named Etheric Template Clearing from Australian healer Rod Campbell. It is a technique that is free-flowing and allows much creativity in the practitioner's hand movements. Its purpose is to clear and vitalize the energetic grids which are the framework for structures of the physical body.

As the practitioner moves her open hands from the client's physical body outward toward the outermost level of the field, she may sense what feels like tangled hair or congested, uneven energy. Repeated "combing" of these strands results in a gradual "untangling" or clearing of the energy matrix and seems to fortify physical structures of the body. There are no rules for this intervention other than to "follow the energy" until it feels clear and flowing.

Lymphatic Drain

Lymphatic Drain is a full–body, systemic method identified by Janet Mentgen to address lymphatic congestion and immune system disturbances. Many practitioners have found this very effective in releasing post flu symptoms, relieving pain or congestion during a systemic illness, and alleviating the effects of systemic chemotherapy. The steps are numbered in the diagram below to give the reader an idea of the sequence HT practitioners use above the physical body with focused hand movements to bring about relief.

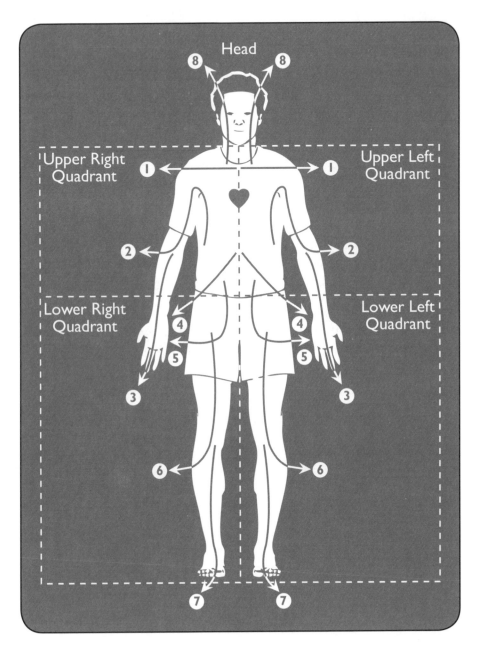

Figure 8.6. Schematic Representation of Lymphatic Drain Sequence.

Invitation to Guidance

Energetic healing at these subtle levels of the human energy field is primarily accomplished as the practitioner attunes to her sense of compassion and her Higher Self. The hand movements are simple and graceful and the feeling of sacredness is palpable. Practitioners learn to invite guidance from spiritual helpers as part of their alignment with all aspects of the multidimensional self. The presence of guides or angels may be perceptible and incredible peace may be felt by both practitioners and clients.

While inviting the presence of spiritual guides to infuse healing light, the practitioner gradually lifts her arms and hands to blend with the sixth layer of the field, the celestial body. All levels of the client's field become ever more filled with light as the practitioner completes movements to the outer layer, the ketheric template. At the seventh layer, which also forms the auric shell around the body, the practitioner gently and consciously begins to follow the shape of the aura with an arc-like gesture slowly outlining the oval shape of the field.

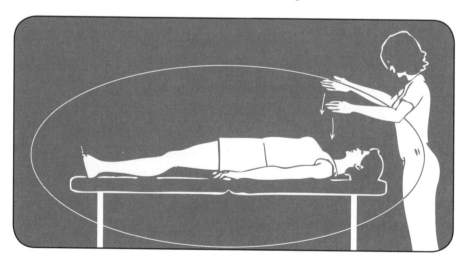

Figure 8.7. Sealing the Outermost Layer of the Field for Closure after a Multidimensional Intervention.

As the practitioner envelopes the outer perimeter of the client's field, she may image or experience gold and silver light flooding from her fingertips to complete the healing intervention. As a final gesture completion, the practitioner moves to the side of the client and holds the seventh level of the field for a period of time while honoring the intention for integration of the healing work. This part of the session may be completed with a bow, a gesture, or prayer of gratitude that blesses the work done together. The client is given some time to integrate before the practitioner offers the grounding gesture. Discussion of the experience and future plans of care are addressed as final steps of the sequence.

Closing Thoughts

The learning that takes place in the Level Three classroom often feels like a quantum leap to many students. They come to appreciate the subtle energetic dimensions of healing and the beautiful, sacred essence of the human being. Many learners seek further practice and time to integrate these new levels of understanding which become more real and natural to them over time.

Once students have completed Level Three, they have learned most of the steps of the methods of the Healing Touch Program and proceed to Level Four to learn practical and specific ways to define themselves as professional energy therapy practitioners. Students move forward to Levels Four and Five by making a commitment to deepen their skills of the standardized methods and sequences taught in the HT Program.

Chapter Notes

1. B.Brennan, *Hands of Light: A guide to healing through the human energy field* (New York: Bantam Books, 1987).

2. B. Brennan, *Light Emerging: The journey of personal healing* (New York: Bantam, 1993).

3. B. Brennan, (1993) *op.cit.*, 288.

Chapter 9

Principles of Therapeutic Practice at Levels Four and Five

Cynthia Hutchison, DNSc, RN, MSN, HTCP/I

Until one is committed there is hesitancy, the chance to draw back, always ineffectiveness. ...the moment one definitely commits oneself, then Providence moves too. All sorts of things occur to help one that would never otherwise have occurred.

—Wolfgang v. Goethe

Levels Four and Five of the Healing Touch Program deepen the learner's understanding of energy therapy. They are also designed to help students who desire to go beyond the basics and wish to become established practitioners. These two courses provide students with knowledge that will help launch them in developing a professional HT practice, either privately or within conventional healthcare settings.

By the end of Level Three coursework, participants have learned to apply the Healing Touch Sequence and methods in their sessions and to incorporate principles and concepts of HT. Ethical practice concerns have been addressed, discussed and reinforced throughout. Students who continue to resonate with Healing Touch often pursue completion of all five levels and proceed on to the HT Certification process that is internationally recognized.

In this chapter, we'll discuss concepts of the upper level courses to describe the professionalism of the HT Program and the

personal development required to become a Healing Touch Certified
Practitioner (HTCP).

Treatment Exchanges in Retreat Settings

HT founder Janet Mentgen and her colleagues designed Levels
Four and Five to be experienced in retreat centers over the course
of three or four days. This enables students to be away from their
normal activities and focus fully on taking their next steps in an environment of reflection and growth. The nature and beauty of retreat
centers also hold devotional energy to support participants as they
integrate information and learning toward becoming professional energy medicine practitioners.

Level Four has ten units of approximately three hours each including evening meetings. The schedule is intensive and fulfilling. There
is a pleasant rhythm that alternates for each individual attending the
workshop. Roles change, so learners experience receiving HT methods
and sequences both as clients and as practitioners. Unlike the previous HT classes where students are encouraged to change partners after
each practice of a new method, learners pair up with one other student
to deepen comprehension of case study methods.

It is essential for learners to experience working with a specific
fellow student who serves in the role of client while they also work as
a practitioner going through all the pertinent steps of several sessions
and sequences. Specific focus is on the intake interview and updates,
four client sessions that each include the ten-step HT sequence (as
described in chapter 5) and a discharge plan. All of these activities
are documented as they would be in a professional practice and are
discussed as case study samples in the classroom with care taken to
honor confidentiality.

Although participants learn case study methods in the exchanges
within the classroom environment, problem identification and treat-

ments are very real. In the client role, participants take off their student hats and allow themselves to fully experience what it is like to be treated by a Healing Touch practitioner, albeit, with someone who is, for the time being, an apprentice. They also become more aware of their own healing issues and continue on their journey toward higher degrees of wellness with a deeper level of awareness.

When the partners switch roles, the one in the practitioner role consciously switches gears to being a heart-centered, attentive HT practitioner. The intention of the person in the practitioner role is to facilitate body-mind-spirit healing in the recipient. By the end of the Level Four class, the partners in each dyad have attained valuable new skills and are more aware of their abilities and strengths as well as their needs for further learning. While some partnerships result in long-term friendships, other partnerships manifest equally valuable teachings, such as working with someone who has challenging traits. The instructor and students set the intention at the beginning for each dyad to be a perfect learning opportunity. As in real life, partners often mirror to each other what they need to see within themselves.

Major Content Areas

Naturally, there are additional major content areas to be learned in the advanced levels. Review of all the methods brings sharing of adventures that practitioners had while implementing some of the methods in their work or home settings. There is ample time for demonstrations, specific questions and answers to deepen learning. This is always a welcome part as the majority of students by this time have developed their "favorite" HT methods and forgotten others. Other less-used methods are revisited to demonstrate relevant applications.

Another important content area of Level Four is the review of each element of the HT Sequence and the necessary skills to document case progress and planning. Instructors use the wide range of students' backgrounds to create a teamwork environment for learning. Group support encourages students to share insights, highlights, and to discuss questions.

Heart-centeredness, so integral to HT practice, is also evident in the HT classroom where less-confident students receive support and encouragement from more seasoned fellow students and the well-practiced instructor. Class mentors also attend the retreats to assist and come from the growing cadre of certified practitioners who have active HT practices and wish to become instructors. In an environment where it is safe to be oneself, participants can assess themselves honestly and commit to the self-insight needed to facilitate healing on behalf of their future patients.

Professional issues are also highlighted in Level Four. While many students are eager to learn the skills of developing private practices, others want to know how to establish themselves as HT practitioners in the healthcare facilities where they are already working. Integration takes place by weaving together the principles, methods and sequences that have been introduced in the first three levels. HT practitioner-apprentices work to develop business plans and visions that exemplify their ethical, clinical and healing ideals.

Toward the end of the Level Four class, several students share case study presentations of the sessions they completed. Everyone listens carefully to learn how presenters integrate their client management skills. Careful feedback from fellow students, class mentors and the instructors is intended to empower leaning. This experience serves as a preparation for the months ahead prior to completing the Program with Level Five.

Two additional techniques are taught at Level Four and described briefly here-- the Full Body Connection and the Etheric Vitality Meditation.

The Full Body Connection

The Full Body Connection is a more advanced version of the Chakra Connection[1] taught in Level One (and described in chapter 6). This method includes its principles with a slightly different intention. Here, not only are the major chakras and minor chakras of the limb joints connected, energized and balanced, but the practitioner also includes the soles of the feet, the palms of the hands and the major organs on the trunk of the body.

The intention of this method is to relieve congestion in all dimensions of the human energy field, energize the organs, and facilitate the restoration of physical and energetic bodies. It is a deeply meditative practice. The practitioner generally uses a sequenced set of hand positions. There is also the liberty to add other hand placements in response to the client's energy patterns.

The Etheric Vitality Meditation

Janet Mentgen had a deep appreciation for the teachings of Doskolos, a Greek healer from Cypress who practiced as a hands-on spiritual healer in the middle and later part of the twentieth century. His biography as a healer was recorded by anthropologist Kyriacos Markides who worked closely with Doskolos and authored three books about his work. In *Homage to the Sun,*[2] a healing meditation is described that Janet adapted for the HT curriculum and named the Etheric Vitality Meditation. This meditation firmly grounds the practitioner in his body and into the earth while simultaneously facilitating connection to the Cosmos and its spiritual healing power.

Etheric Vitality is a 15 to 20 minute meditation in which the practitioner's hands remain still above the client's crown center. Experiences students report in their exchanges include a feeling of expansion of their fields, movement to higher vibrational levels, ability to tap into higher wisdom, and a sense of oneness with her partner and/or all of Creation.

The Apprenticeship Year

Students are prepared for their upcoming experience as a Practitioner-Apprentice by thoroughly reviewing the homework, often referred to as "growthwork," that needs to be done before attending Level Five. Eight valuable assignments need to be completed in order to graduate from the Program. Many students acknowledge the period of apprenticeship between Levels Four and Five as a time of accelerated personal and professional growth. The assignments are:

1. Creation of a Professional Profile Notebook of the student's own design with visual and written overviews of the apprentice's work in her community

2. Submission of a Professional Resume for presenting oneself professionally

3. Evidence of 100 or more documented HT sessions using the ten-step HT sequence and all the HTP methods from the standard curriculum to help develop clinical expertise

4. Submission of reports of receiving ten different holistic modalities to assure that the student is personally acquainted with a variety of holistic methods and has networked with other holistic practitioners

5. Presentation of at least seven reflective summaries of books read from the bibliography given about Healing Touch, Energy Medicine/Holistic Health Care, Quantum Physics, Spiritual Development, Journaling/Self Care, Professional Development and Ethics

6. Participation in a Supervised Mentorship with a HT Certified Practitioner (HTCP) which includes observations of the mentee giving sessions as well as administration of a session to the mentor

7. <u>Participation in Professional Networking and a Community Project</u> to show ability to create outreach into the community with professional colleagues and community members

8. <u>Submission of a written case study</u> to show adequate clinical skills over four or more sessions incorporating all the essential aspects of the core curriculum and case study concepts.

Students are asked to assess their current skills and limitations and to participate in guided visualizations to imagine their futures. The goals may also include becoming a Certified Instructor or taking a leadership role in bringing HT, energetic healing and holistic healthcare to specific populations.

An important element of the apprenticeship time is the supportive relationship with a mentor that begins after completing the fourth level. Students who wish to continue toward graduation are required to identify one or more mentors who will guide them during the apprenticeship period. Selection of a mentor is vital since the student will have monthly mentor contacts and progress evaluations. Students are instructed in criteria for selecting mentors who will best support their journey toward course completion. Mentors are certified practitioners who give feedback to the mentees about written assignments, provide guidance in case study management, discuss clinical issues, and monitor mentees' professional growth and self -care. Mentors assure that the student understands and abides by the HTP Code of Ethics and Statement of Scope of Practice.

Different models of mentorship are possible. Students living in metropolitan areas may have ample opportunities for HT practice groups and other courses. Those who live in outlying regions where HT is not established, may need to set up long distance mentorships via Internet, Skype or telephone.

Level Five as Graduation from the HT Program

When the apprentice completes most or all of the requirements for graduation, she/he attends the Level Five course. The time period may vary from six months to several years. As for Level Four, it is taught in a retreat setting to foster learning and integration without the distractions of everyday life. This course has been described as a joyous culmination which focuses on personal sharing of completing the eight assignments given. Case study presentations, group healing sessions, one-on-one exchanges, and preparation for international certification round out the curriculum. Most students make a point of expressing gratitude for how meaningful the assignments were constructed to support their professional and personal development.

Often, Level Four and Five classes take place in the same location so there may be networking between the two groups. When they occur simultaneously, a block of time may is given for more advanced students to share their experiences with lower level students, to cheer them on and make recommendations for the upcoming apprenticeship year.

In the first portion of Level Five, students share their personal journeys from the apprenticeship year and networking projects in their communities. A favorite activity is sharing the Professional Profile Notebooks each student brings. Attendees enjoy viewing the pages of the notebooks which they can present as autobiographical stories. Many graduates continue to use their notebooks as a practical resource to share with potential clients, health care administrators, and colleagues. Regarding ethics, real and theoretical ethical issues that come up in the practice of Healing Touch are discussed in stimulating small group and large group formats.

A block of time is set aside for group healing sessions to experience receiving treatments from two or more people at once. Getting on a treatment table to "receive" is welcome after the many other hours of intellectual study in the classroom.

The entire class meets to hear sample case studies and make helpful, insightful comments. Final aspects of Level Five include individual meetings between students and the instructor to support any further preparation for graduation and/or certification. Flexibility in this completion phase of the Program is important to support the many students who are wearing multiple hats in their lives, such as being a parent, grandparent, college student, employee or caregiver to elderly parents. A warm-hearted graduation ceremony takes place as a farewell.

In summary, Level Five brings students to graduation and to receiving the hard-earned title of Healing Touch Practitioner. By the time the core curriculum is successfully completed, learners have demonstrated competencies, professionalism, ethical sensitivity, appropriate applications of HT methods and sequences within a case study framework, ability to network, and an orientation toward service in their communities.

Chapter Notes

1. B. Joy, *Joy's Way: A map for the transformational journey* (New York: G.P. Putnam's Sons, 1979).

2. K. Markides, *Homage to the Sun: The wisdom of the magus of Strovolos* (New York: Arcana, 1987) 58-60.

Section III

Healing Touch as a Vital Participant in Today's Healthcare

Chapter 10
Healing Touch in Relation to Integrative Healthcare

If I told patients to raise their blood levels of immune globulins or killer T-cells, no one would know how. But if I can teach them to love themselves and others fully, the same change happens automatically. The truth is: Love heals.

-Bernie Siegel

Healing Touch has become a vital component in the broad range of complementary modalities currently grouped under the rubric of "integrative medicine." Until 1980 and 1981, when the American Holistic Medical Association (AHMA) and the American Holistic Nurses Association (AHNA) were formed, respectively, there was no official public forum for the many healing modalities that fell outside the conventional medical care model known in the West. Holistic concepts, unifying physical, emotional, mental, and spiritual dimensions of the whole person, sent a breath of fresh air to the nation's increasingly technically oriented healthcare system. Increasing numbers of patients began seeking alternatives to the conventional treatments of surgery, chemotherapy, and medication. Longer life spans made it clear that different methods were needed to address issues prevalent in the nation's maturing population. These issues include diagnoses of lifelong disease such as arthritis, heart disease, and diabetes, conditions linked to severe and chronic pain, depression, anxiety, and other symptoms frequently associated with aging.

Current estimates are that more than 80 percent of the American population turns to one or more forms of complementary modalities to find physical and psychological relief. By contrast, a more conservative national statistics study cites that at least 36 percent of American adults are using alternative therapies.[1] The trend toward use of complementary modalities is significant, especially since most payments for services have to come out of pocket and are not covered by most insurers.

Nursing has played a major role in this shift toward complementary modalities since it is an integrative science based on understandings from many disciplines such as anatomy, physiology, biology, physics, chemistry, psychology, spirituality, and related social sciences. One might correctly state that nursing is holistic or integrative by definition. The AHNA enjoys more than five thousand members, and their research publications have further identified and enriched the many usages of holistic concepts in the delivery of nursing care. Canada and Australia, two countries that embraced Healing Touch soon after its inception, also have active holistic nurses associations, as do many other countries worldwide.

Healing Touch has always been a modality belonging within the holistic framework. It shines brightest as a complement, or adjunct, to conventional and other alternative modalities because it is based on holistic principles, the nursing process and Watson's Caring Theory.[2] It also has a growing body of studies and research (described in chapter 4) to support its presence in mainstream healthcare.

For hospitalized patients, HT offers compassionate and intentional human touch from a skilled professional or trained volunteer to help alleviate pain, diminish pre or post procedural anxiety, or effect needed relaxation. In other medical facilities such as the increasingly utilized one-day surgical centers and outpatient clinics, HT can serve as the brief humanistic connection between medical interventions and patients' psychological needs. In palliative or hospice settings, HT practitioners, who may be nurses, social workers, or lay volunteers, provide deeper levels of emotional and spiritual care to those suffering with serious long-term illness or those in the process of dying. In these many institutional settings, HT practitioners are closely aligned with physicians and ancillary healthcare personnel as part of an integrative treatment team. A recent high-caliber study demonstrated a $500,000 annual savings to the related hospital due to early hospital discharge for patients who received HT for anxiety relief.

In private care settings, which are attracting more and more HT caregivers, practitioners offer individualized treatment protocols to address a number of issues related to client desires for enhanced well-being. To increase their effectiveness, these practitioners also establish strong professional referral networks consisting of qualified specialists who bring needed and appropriate resources to their clients. For example, many clients come to HT practitioners seeking alternative care because they have experienced the limitations of the conventional medical model, which says in essence, "There is nothing further we can do." Worse, some clients have been led to believe that their symptoms are only in their mind. These clients may still be in need of medical care to manage pain or disability, and the HT practitioner can effect referral to holistically oriented physicians, naturopaths, homeopaths, body workers, and related integrative practitioners.

Many HT practitioners spontaneously uncover emotional trauma of which the client had only premonitions or was totally unaware. This can occur because trauma appears to be stored in the biofield, its layers, meridians, and/or chakras, and can surface spontaneously during a session. It is essential for the practitioner to know skilled psychotherapists who can effectively treat clients suffering emotional trauma. (See appendix E for psychotherapists who practice in the new field of energy psychology.) Often, the sessions with a referral counselor are held for a limited time period while the relationship with the HT practitioner continues to provide ongoing support and aftercare over a much longer time. This serves as a collaborative example of two or more practitioners synergistically supporting a client's healing.

Making appropriate referrals is thus an essential component to building one's reputation as an effective practitioner. It enhances rather than diminishes the practice and builds relationships, not only between the client and HT practitioner, but also between holistic practitioners in the community. Furthermore, the practice of referrals ensures HT's presence as a team player in the integrative model of healthcare that is currently evolving.

Developments Toward Integrative Healthcare

A bit of history is helpful here in understanding the evolution of holistic, integrative thinking as a reflection of a growing public trend. The National Institutes of Health (NIH) has been the organizational bastion of conventional medical care in America. Its precepts are built on allopathic theories, which, by definition, honor only medical interventions that counter or oppose the patient's disease process via decisive interventions such as surgery or utilization of chemicals. Rationalistic thinking of cause and effect ("this" medication or treatment for "that" symptom) dominates the conventional medical paradigm.

As a result of a consumer-led demand to legitimize other approaches in the 1980s, the NIH established a small office of alternative (meaning non-allopathic) medicine. This office grew steadily and, by the beginning of the twenty-first century, a joint panel of leaders in conventional and in holistic care practices decided the word "alternative" suggested a limited "either/or" choice to the patient. Use of the word "complementary" came into prominence as it captured the meaning of "complement," an adjunctive modality that serves to fill out or complete other practice interventions. Thus, the National Center for Complementary and Alternative Medicine (NCCAM), was established to acknowledge, standardize, and initiate study of the diverse elements of the seemingly unruly non-allopathic endeavors. NCCAM defined seven areas of these complements or adjuncts to conventional medical care.[3] They are:

1. Bioelectromagnetic applications

2. Alternative systems of medical practice—including Oriental medicine, acupuncture, Ayurveda, homeopathy, and Native American medicine

3. Manual healing methods—massage, somatic therapies, and chiropractic interventions

4. Pharmacological and biological treatments not yet accepted by mainstream medicine such as medical chelation

5. Herbal medicines

6. Treatments focusing on diet and nutrition in the prevention and treatment of chronic diseases

7. Body-mind interventions such as yoga, prayer, mental healing, and energy modalities.

Because the last category cannot as yet be objectively measured, it has been labeled "frontier medicine." It is, of course, somewhat humbling to realize that HT is but a subset of CAM, which, in turn, is the focus of only one of the many centers within NIH. The NCCAM budget is thin by comparison to the massive budgets for other NIH centers such as the Center for the Study of Heart Disease, but it has been steadily gaining and increasing public interest since its inception.

The inclusion of "energy modalities" as part of CAM is significant mainly because it acknowledges that HT has a known place within complementary healthcare. With this recognition, however, HT is also coming under increasing scrutiny from powers very dedicated to the allopathic medical model and its financially successful dominance on the patient care scene. The zeal of many practitioners to share HT with everyone must be tempered with careful attention to theory, scientific reasoning, the presence of ongoing research, and viable, effective organizational and ethical structures. As a friend of energy therapies, leading complementary legal advisor and healthcare ethicist, Michael Cohen warns, "Make no mistake: energy therapies still occupy a legal gray zone for many professions and in many states ... it can be [very] important to consult an attorney for legal advice regarding the offering of energy therapies within a particular practice setting."[4] Because of this need for caution, the HT Program has carefully set up resources for ethics and practice guidelines (covered later in this book). In 1994, the HT Program also created a department of research with its own website, www.HealingTouchResearch.com. In addition, it is actively engaged in seeking accreditation for HT from national organizations that oversee and validate hundreds of healthcare certification programs.

In an effort to legitimize and give recognition to energy modalities, the trend has been toward calling energy-based interventions "energy medicine" (undoubtedly with an eye to the medical model and its persistent "medicine" language). Cohen defines energy medicine as the "subset of therapies within the spectrum of complementary and alternative medical therapies that primarily are based on the projection of information, consciousness, and/or intentionality to the patient."[5] His definition encompasses the many permutations of energy-oriented approaches, which include energy psychology, medical intuition, Therapeutic Touch, Healing Touch, Reiki, Oriental medicine, distance healing and many others. This is a somewhat limited view of HT practice even though it comes from an acknowledged authority in the field of CAM law.

The intention in HT of aligning with the unlimited supply of energy in the Universal Field is facilitated by the practitioner's centering and focus. In a recent personal communication with me, HT practitioner and instructor Janna Moll clarified: "I think what we are doing is holding a space for clients where they can connect to their divine and perfect expression—and inviting them into this as much as possible. It is not about *my* information or *my* consciousness, and certainly not *my* goals for the client, but about *their* own needs and desires—from a place of wholeness."

In February 2009, the Summit on Integrative Medicine was held in the nation's capital to initiate change in perspectives of healthcare toward increased wellness and prevention. Senator Harkin and his Committee to Advise President Obama expressed their wish for a proposed name change from NCCAM to Center for Integrative Health. While this name change may take some time to go through necessary government channels, the trend toward integrative healthcare and primary prevention in medical care centers is unmistakable.

Christine (Tina) Devoe, HT practitioner and instructor, attended the summit and reported her perceptions of this important meeting in *Energy Magazine*.[6] Like many nurses, she is an example of HT participation in the growing integrative medicine initiatives that can be seen throughout the country. She combines training in touch therapies with her holistic nursing practice to empower clients. She draws from her twenty years' experience in maternal and child health nursing to practice at the Department of Integrative Medicine at Calvert Memorial Hospital. Tina pioneered the practice of Healing Touch and massage there and has written coursework to include "Holistic Approaches to Wellness and Medical Massage" for the College of Southern Maryland. Through her teaching and workshops, Tina aims to increase knowledge of the human biofield and its relevance to health while also "growing" a new HT community.

Models of Integrative Healthcare

HT practitioner Lynn O'Donnell reports on an important sign of the interest in integrative healthcare.[7] She describes the decisions from her Veterans Administration hospital to approve HT presence in their five-day-a-week interdisciplinary pain clinic. In addition, the project will require data collection for a research protocol to officially measure and research the effects of HT in pain reduction. It is to be hoped that, with more such initiatives, we will see an increasing number of veterans receiving HT. Administering HT within veteran care facilities would be a nurturing and supportive way to welcome our servicemen and women back from the war fronts!

Another example of a dynamic integrative healthcare model is taking place at the Scripps Center for Integrative Medicine.[8] Located in La Jolla near San Diego, California, the center offers instructional courses in a six-week program for coronary preventive care as well as postcoronary recovery using the integrative medical model of Dr. Dean Ornish. In addition, its primary interventional cardiologist and leading nurse are HT practitioners who teach HT principles and treatments to the patients throughout the course.

Long-time HT practitioner and instructor Kathy Sinnett founded her own integrative healthcare center, the Sinnett Holistic Health Center, in Livonia, Michigan. For fifteen years until her recent retirement, she operated this successful center, which offers massage, spirit release work, reflexology, meditation and classes in Feng Shui, and other complementary modalities in addition to regular HT treatments and basic and advanced classes. For the past ten years, the center has continued under the guidance of Kathy's dynamic partners who are also HT practitioners.

Many other models that combine conventional medical care with complementary modalities exist. One example of a successfully operating integrative center is Whole Health Chicago.[9] Larry Stoler, a past president of ACEP, practices clinical psychology with his unique specialties of energy psychology and medical qigong. The clinic is an independent integrative medical center in which a large complement of practitioners unites to formulate the best outcomes for their clients. The staff includes an internist physician, a chiropractor, an acupuncturist, a clinical psychologist, a nutritionist, a homeopath, a massage therapist, an herbalist and flower essence expert, a physical therapist, and an HT practitioner in the person of Katie Oberlin. They have worked together over seven years to bring patients the best from both conventional medicine and CAM approaches.

Oberlin writes about her work at the center: "I see over three hundred clients annually—some for one visit; others for a series of visits over the course of a few months; others come a few times, take several months off and then come in again; and others see me on a regular basis. Most of my clients are referred to me by the internist; I also receive referrals from the chiropractor and psychologist as well as other practitioners and staff members. When a patient sees the internist for the first time, he puts together a Healing Path for the patient that includes relevant referrals.

Susan's Story

Oberlin writes, "A client I'll call Susan, single and thirty-five years old, came referred by the psychologist for depression, which had begun several years before when her mother passed away and she became estranged from her siblings. She also experienced significant fibromyalgia pain and chronic fatigue. Her work situation had been very stressful lately with a boss who had very high demands and worries about layoffs. During our first Healing Touch session, I introduced Susan to Healing Touch, using some PowerPoint slides to describe the energy system, explain what energy healing is, what is meant by a 'holistic' approach, the goals of Healing Touch and how it might help her, and what she might experience during each session. Her stated goals were to decrease stress, pain, and fatigue and develop a happier outlook on life. She also expressed interest in rekindling a spiritual connection that had waned over the years. Based on her goals and my energetic assessment, we began with Mind Clearing, followed by Magnetic Clearing to clear emotional congestion. The session ended with a Chakra Connection. Susan felt much calmer, was happy to receive a handout on 'Self-care After a Healing Touch Session,' and expressed gratitude for having found a place that finally understood her healthcare needs.

"Since that first session, I have been seeing Susan every week or two. I complete the full Healing Touch sequence at every appointment, and choose techniques based on her goals and my energetic assessment. Throughout each session, I simply open myself to be a 'channel of light and love,' and allow the energy to guide me. During one particular session, she mentioned that she really missed her mother. My intuition told me that she had never fully made the transition to allow acceptance of her loss, so we did a Sacred Chakra Spread, followed by Magnetic Clearing. Afterward, Susan expressed feeling 'much more at peace.' Susan has experienced many ups and downs, but now feels she is moving in a positive direction. She practices the Self Chakra Connection almost every day, has joined a yoga class, and has a more relaxed outlook on her challenges. At a recent appointment, she said she was surprised when a coworker mentioned that things don't seem to bother her as much as they used to."

***

Integrative models are increasing rapidly as the public recognizes the need for preventive healthcare long before the onset of disease. In fact, many dysfunctions can be prevented or postponed with appropriate early interventions, such as stress management and wellness programs. HT in the private sector plays a major role in enhancing personal well-being and relieving anxiety; this, in turn, enhances immune functioning so the breakdown of tissue can be prevented or slowed. Gone are the days when people had to wait to "get sick" before learning about ways to maintain their health! In institutional treatment settings, HT is a major player in relieving pre and post procedural/surgical stress and effecting positive outcomes for rapid healing. In every life stage, HT practices can offer relief and paths to self-care, as we will explore further in chapter 13.

In spite of this growing direction in national healthcare, there are elements that wish to diminish or disprove the efficacy of energy methods. Scrutiny of complementary modalities is intensified as major portions of the healthcare dollar are reapportioned to complementary modalities. Being astutely aware of these realities, HT organizational and ethics structures serve to enhance and protect the diverse clinical practices of HT practitioners.

Importance of HT's Organizational and Ethical Structures

What you do not want someone to
do to you, do not do to others ...
What you do not want someone to
say to you, do not say to others ...
What you do not want someone to
say about you, do not say about others

—Kerstin Warkentin, ACEP coordinator in Germany

The support of national professional organizations in establishing and validating innovative complementary modalities such as HT cannot be minimized. The HT Professional Association (see the following text and appendix A) is the representative body for HT practitioners just as the American Nurses Association represents nurses and the American Medical Association represents physicians. In the case of interventions which are not yet validated by strict adherence to quantitative scientific research, as is the case with HT and "energy medicine modalities" in general, a professional association becomes the "defensible majority" in legal terms.[10] This means that a representative group of experienced and competent (also considered "sane") professionals acknowledges and utilizes the identified practices. "The mind/body therapies that fall under the CAM umbrella will be more readily accepted as viable, ethical, and authentic if they have established ethics codes, educational and certification requirements, research information, and national platforms."[11] Healing Touch currently has all of these except a national platform; however, the voice of consumers and holistic practitioners is growing louder each year thanks to research, consumer empowerment, and practitioners who are enthusiastically educating the public and their clients.

In concerted efforts to stay ahead of the growing diversity of healthcare options, HT has developed major policies to cover ethical issues such as scope of practice, credentialing, handling of malpractice, mediation of conflicts, and, above all, risk management to reduce the likelihood of adverse reactions from other professions. The HT Code of Ethics (see appendix B) is the current working document for the HT Program and is constantly scrutinized and updated by the Ethics Committee under the leadership of Janna Moll, MSN, RN, HTCP/I.

The ethical standards of a program certainly demonstrate the difference between programs positioned to align with allopathic methods and those of an integrative, holistic approach. The fact that the Healing Touch Program came out of the founders' training as nurses and their alignment with holistic healthcare created the foundation for a program that is fashioned on similar ethics and standards. The principles of integrative healthcare ethics augment recognition of HT in mainstream healthcare. The principles of client-centered, holistic care include:[12]

Treat others, not only clients, but also colleagues, with respect.

- Practice confidentiality.

- Do no harm.

- Protect the vulnerable client.

- Consider the power differential in a healing setting.

- Practice mutual goal setting.

- Honor the client's right of choice.

- Seek consultation for difficult issues.

- Be honest about your training and background.

- Refrain from exorbitant promises.

- Validate the client's progress.

- Use referral resources as needed.

Ethics of a program and individual ethics may differ since a personal sense of values to support one's decision-making is unique to the individual practitioner. One way to gauge your personal ethics is to evaluate what you might do when no one is looking. (Some people, for example, drive their cars very differently when no police are around!) Our personal code of ethics influences our social and professional contacts, behavioral goals, and choices about health and self-care.

As chair of the HT Ethics Committee, Janna Moll writes, "The ethical standards and codes of a program or discipline in the field of energy medicine create the framework for the discipline's practitioners. When these codes are enforced and upheld by a committee of the group's independent, trained practitioners and instructors, the consensus of the committee becomes the voice for the discipline. This voice will uphold the behavioral standards for the discipline's practitioners and instructors. This is a very important point since a practitioner who upholds the HT Code of Ethics will be protected or assisted by the organization. Published, strong, and defended ethics help create a stable foundation for our practice and go a long way toward a legally defensible position for HT."

Transparency is a very important practice for building trust in any discipline or group. When rules and procedures are clearly stated and those making the decisions are known, members of the group can feel secure that guidelines are in place and uniformly followed. Fairness within the profession serves as a guiding principle. Since most ethical breaches are not huge, blatant ones, but little blurrings, an established structure within HT for guiding and educating practitioners is essential.

Public trust is built on knowledge about the educational and practice requirements for someone who calls her/himself a HT certified practitioner. Many people with minimal training may call themselves "energy healers" as a way to elevate their self-esteem or professional status. It is recommended that students of energy modalities refer to themselves as exactly what they are, "student," until full credentialing is achieved. It is a public right to know what the HT credential means and to base selection of appropriate caregivers on that information.

Public Recognition of Healing Touch's Certification Component

A discipline's certification program essentially defines the minimal or foundational requirements for its practice. Since the beginning of HT's certification program in 1993, many HT practitioners have extended their practices to include broader or more specialized applications and endeavors, as we will see in chapters 11 and 12. Nonetheless, the certification credential is the definitive standard that specifies for public recognition the arenas of sanctioned HT practice.

One of the main questions asked regarding any certification program is, "Who accredits your program?" In today's complex web of healthcare opportunities, certification increases in value when there are numerous layers of accountability in place. For example, physicians attend an accredited school and take state/specialty/national examinations, which are also overseen by national accreditation, in order to obtain their licenses to practice. The National Organization for Competency Assurance (NOCA), with its National Commission for Certifying

Agencies (NCCA), oversees many of the healthcare certifications in the United States, especially technical and nursing certifications. Therefore, becoming accredited under NOCA, a work currently in progress, will put the Healing Touch Program in alignment with certification standards that are accepted and expected in healthcare.

The Healing Touch Program has an autonomous certification board and committee which function at an international level for its worldwide practitioners. This means they function independently from the Healing Touch Program, yet are made up of its professionals and utilize its standards of education and practice. These layers of accountability demonstrate to the world that standards are in place, that these standards are enforced autonomously by the membership organization, and that there is transparent accountability at each level.

The Healing Touch Professional Association (HTPA)

The Healing Touch Professional Association (HTPA) is a worldwide membership association, created to unite and give a voice to the Healing Touch community. Led by executive director Sharon Robbins, it invites active participation in the international growth of Healing Touch.[13]

HTPA provides members the support of a strong professional organization with many benefits such as a self-managed member directory, a "members only" message/forum board, new and expanding opportunities to participate in special interest projects, online business support and education, HT service events, and professional and general liability insurance for qualified students, practitioners, and instructors of HT and other energy modalities.

HTPA's vision is to give the best service to its members while continually expanding member benefits. Members vote on a regular basis to make choices about moving HTPA forward, and the leadership team is representative of HT professionals worldwide. Networking and opportunities to give back to others are offered and encouraged among this important professional group.

With membership in HTPA, HT practitioners are in the best position to be incorporated into integrative medical or mainstream healthcare clinic settings. CAM modalities that do not have national or state level organizations run the risk of being subject to regulations from outside, often by competitive agencies who could limit or ban a modality from being utilized. Healthcare freedom guaranteeing equal access to conventional and complementary/integrative modalities is not considered a right in most states. As of this writing, seven states have passed healthcare freedom legislation, and the legislative process is under way in many more.[14]

Healing Touch Worldwide Foundation

The Healing Touch Worldwide Foundation receives and distributes funds that assist, encourage, and advance the philosophy, objectives, and techniques of Healing Touch.[15] Over the last twelve years, it has enjoyed significant growth from a small, Colorado-based foundation to one that impacts lives around the globe. In the past seven years, the foundation has granted approximately $115,000 for service projects and research. Grants have served low-income, underinsured, and non–English speaking individuals. Research programs have analyzed the effect of Healing Touch in a variety of settings. The foundation's vision is to be the benchmark for excellence in funding Healing Touch research and outreach programs, spreading Healing Touch to communities throughout the world.

HT is a central player in the fast-growing paradigm of integrative healthcare and the specific specialty area called energy medicine. Integrative medicine combines multiple therapies with the goal of enhancing optimal health; holistic medicine emphasizes approaching the patient as an individual who lives within an environment, a web of life that impacts client and caregiver health. Thus, "Integrative Holistic Medicine is the art and science of healing that addresses care of the whole person: body, mind, and spirit."[16] As part of this integrative and holistic healthcare model, HT practitioners provide the much-needed "missing link" between rapid advances in technology and the very real personal needs of the human being.

As an example of these human needs, consider how technology is making great advances in diabetic care. Blood glucose monitoring is sophisticated and easy, diet patterns are readily available anywhere including on the Internet, diabetes educational classes are offered in most communities, and individualized prescriptions for medication are well-known and standardized. But who facilitates patient compliance? Who handles resistance to protocols? Who helps the patient integrate what the disease means to her total lifestyle? In present-day mainstream health care, it is rare to find a person to assist clients in handling the emotional tasks life-altering disease mandates.

By assisting the energy being of the patient, HT practitioners develop bridges to understanding disease and its personal impact. Through the unconditional acceptance present from the intentional, centered HT practitioner, the patient can learn to accept herself and engage in self-care that will enhance self-healing and overall health.

Chapter Notes

1. P. M. Barnes, B. Bloom, and R. Nahin, "Statistics on CAM use in the USA," Washington, DC: National Statistical Report #12, 2007.

2. J. Watson, *Nursing: The philosophy and science of caring* (Boulder, CO:

University Press of Colorado, 2008).

3. M. H. Cohen, *Future Medicine* (Ann Arbor, MI: University of Michigan Press, 2003).

4. D. Hover-Kramer with M. Murphy, *Creating Right Relationships* (Port Angeles, WA: Behavioral Health Consultants, 2007), xx.

5. *Ibid.*, 21.

6. C. Devoe, "The Washington Integrative Healthcare Summit" *HT Energy Magazine* 33(April 2009).

7. L. O'Donnell, personal communication (4/15/09).

8. For more information contact (858) 652-5400 or e-mail med.edu@ scrippshealth.org.

9. L. Stoler, personal communication (4/25/09); www.wholehealthchicago.com.

10. Hover-Kramer with Murphy, *op.cit.*, 28–29.

11. I*bid.*, 28.

12. This is by no means an exhaustive list of ethical principles honored in most social service humanistic disciplines. The principles are elaborated in C. Barstow, *The Right Use of Power* (Boulder, CO: Many Realms Press, 2005).

13. Contact Healing Touch Program Professional Association at www.HTProfessionalAssociation.com and also see HT organizational chart in appendix A.

14. Retrieved April 30, 2009, from American Board of Integrative and Holistic Medicine (ABIHM), www.holisticboard.org.

15. Healing Touch Worldwide Foundation website: www. htwfoundation.org.

16. ABIHM www.holisticboard.org, *op.cit.*

Chapter 11

Healing Touch in Relation to the Human Life Cycle

The universal human journey is one of becoming conscious of our power and how to use that power. Becoming conscious of the responsibility inherent in the power of choice represents the core of this journey.

—Caroline Myss

Healing Touch treatments have universal appeal because they can readily be applied at every stage of the human life cycle. Now that HT has been in existence for over twenty years, it's possible to describe the contributions of creative HT practitioners to people at different phases of life.

Practitioners of HT's central philosophy of human caring reach out not only to their identified clients and patients but also to their families, neighbors, friends, and their communities. Less formal, ad hoc contacts may consist of one or more brief interventions to bring about physical and emotional relief and deep levels of relaxation. Many advanced practitioners offer classes in their communities around identified themes to enhance participants' wellness.

Because of HT's strong affiliation with holistic, integrative healthcare principles, as discussed in the previous chapter, HT can readily be visualized in a wide range of integrative healthcare environments in addition to hospitals, outpatient clinics, home care settings, hospices, and private practices. The reported and documented effects of HT interventions have generally been relief from anxiety, increased relaxation, decreased pain sensation, improved immune system functioning, and an enhanced sense of well-being including deepening spiritual connection. Significant, of course, is that these desirable outcomes are achieved without much financial cost, invasive medical procedures, or known side effects. Recipients of HT frequently remark on how safe and nurtured they feel as they participate in receiving HT for a single meeting or a series of sessions.

The quest to understand the mechanisms for these outcomes continues via ongoing research, some of it funded privately and some funded by NIH's CAM center. Very recent studies are demonstrating the efficacy of enhanced well-being in increasing immune system function through mechanisms of gene expression. A recent study at Harvard described how the activation of the relaxation response (one of the most frequent effects seen in HT) actually allows the protein sheath surrounding genetic material in each cell to open and therefore release life-enhancing genetic messages.[1] The ensuing sense of inner calm, heart rhythm coherence, and peace sends cascading messages to other cells and the electromagnetic information networks of the body.[2] Chemical messages create shifts that permit increasing endorphin levels, which, in turn, accelerate relief of pain and strengthen immune system responses.

With these insights in mind, we can easily see how HT could have applications to wherever people are relation to lifetimes. The human life cycle, broadly speaking, consists of:

- Birth
- Early childhood
- Adolescence
- Adult life with career decisions and establishment of new family life

- Midlife, a time of productivity and moving toward healthy aging
- Elderhood, becoming a mentor
- Death and transition to other levels of consciousness

For most people, these stages occur in a more or less linear fashion. The human life cycle can be influenced in a beneficial way by HT methods at any juncture where there is a need for improved physical health, emotional balance, mental clarity, increased personal esteem, relaxation, improved insight, or a heightened sense of personal empowerment.

Here are some suggestions to stimulate thinking about the life stages and their challenges for which HT practice in some form could be implemented:

- Have you thought about using HT with colicky babies, or to calm anxious nursing mothers? Would HT be relevant to an "expectant family," including the father and, possibly, significant relatives or friends?

- Could HT help an overactive child to switch gears, focus on schoolwork or family activities, or prepare for restful sleep?

- Could HT help adolescents in the throes of "raging hormones" to build a stronger sense of personal identity and emotional balance?

- Could school nurses, counselors, or teachers be equipped with knowledge about energy medicine and HT to support students who are dealing with myriad life challenges?

- Would HT have a place in encouraging knowledge and intuition for healthy making adult choices such as further education, partnerships, and improved interpersonal relationships?

- Are there applications for HT in resolving midlife dilemmas? Would taking time to reflect one's life goals and purpose be helpful?

- Is HT useful in planning the second half of life and finding meaning and significant tasks beyond one's career?

- Can employers of large companies offer more holistic options for employee healthcare plans that include HT? Does HT have a place in community education classes or in recreation centers?

- Can HT be taught to provide relief for chronic conditions that often increase in later life?

- How can HT assist the elderly and those moving toward the end of physical life? Can HT help ensure a peaceful transition to the next levels of consciousness?

Many sensitive and creative HT practitioners have asked and addressed these questions. The goal of this chapter is to describe some of the activities of HT practitioners in these expanded applications. Another goal of our discussion is to consider the many potential opportunities for implementing and teaching HT within the human life cycle.

Dynamics of the Chakras in Relation to Human Development

A number of intuitive healers, including Janet Mentgen,[3] Barbara Brennan,[4] and this author,[5] suggest the chakras function as centers of consciousness that are closely aligned with developmental stages throughout the human life cycle. The chakra sequence (described in chapter 2) is expanded here to show how human psychosocial development approximates each decade of life and is related to the chakras as centers of expanding consciousness. Table 11.1 offers one of the many ways to conceptualize the human life cycle from an energetic perspective.

Chakra Name	Psychological and Social Function	Developmental Task as adapted from the work of Erik Erikson	Approximate Age for Task Completion
Root	Establishing safety and security	Trust vs. Mistrust	Birth to 9 years
Sacral	Understanding feelings and sexuality	Autonomy and Industry vs. Shame and Doubt	10 - 19
Solar Plexus	Ego identity, sense of power	Identity vs. Identity Confusion	20 - 29
Heart	Caring, compassion, forgiveness	Intimacy vs. Isolation	30 - 39
Throat	Self-expression, creativity	Creativity vs. Apathy	40 - 49
Brow	Seeing clearly, insight, clairvoyance	Generativity vs. Stagnation	50 - 59
Crown	Transpersonal awareness, fulfilling the soul's purpose	Integrity vs. Despair	60+

Table 11.1. The chakras related to psychosocial development in an approximate decade of life

Using the model of human life stages first charted by developmental psychologist Erik Erikson,[6] the child's developmental task in the first decade of life is to establish a sense of trust, which corresponds to the sense of safety and security vibrating in a healthy first chakra. The next chakra, the sacral, connects with one's feelings and the ability to choose which elements to release and which to keep, based on balanced emotions. Adolescence is the turbulent time of mastering the emotions, planning ahead, and learning to make good decisions. The third decade of life, in one's twenties, is a time that needs clear thinking with the energy of the solar plexus chakra. Decisions about courses of study, careers, and life partnerships mark this stage of life. Accomplishing the developmental tasks inherent in the lower three chakra energies builds the foundation for a healthy, productive life. Many people never fully master these basic tasks of early life, but until they are accomplished, spiritual and creative work with the energies of the upper chakras will be limited or delayed.

The fourth, the heart chakra, is the pivotal center for advancing the person from self-centered focus on ego needs to reaching out, by giving and receiving, in order to establish true caring relationships. Usually by one's thirties, glimpses of altruism emerge as people build long-term relationships and/or become parents. HT appears to empower practitioners at any age to make this next step in their development by its focus on heart-centered caring. The shift from the love of individual and collective powers to the *power of love* is the major change that must occur in humanity to advance possibilities for world peace.[7]

Once the shift to heart-centered caring has been made, the later decades of personal life become highly creative and increasingly in-tuitive with corresponding integration of the fifth and sixth chakras. The second half of life, usually after fifty, becomes an adventure of ex-ploring new interests or deepening wisdom in the mature adult. This sets the stage for the final decades of life as times of walking more fully in the light of one's Higher Power, expressing the soul's purpose and finding fulfillment.

According to Erikson's later-life model, the culmination of per-sonal growth is mature development of one's generativity and integ-rity.[8] Alternatives to personality expansion with aging are stagnation and despair. Our youth-focused, materially oriented culture suggests that the best years of life are the youthful years when physical beau-ty and vitality are at their peak. A value system that integrates the importance of spiritual, mental, and emotional maturity emphasizes accumulated life experiences that can enhance our being in ever-ex-panding joyful and meaningful activity, wisdom, truth, and compassion. In truth, "Each center has unique gifts for us as we choose to develop and mature. All centers are needed in order to become fully alive in the second half of life."[9]

We note how HT practice exemplifies the goal of a satisfying and fulfilling life—to help oneself by helping others and thereby make the world a better place through caring intention.

Healing Touch with Newborns and their Parents

HT practitioner Rita Kluny's background includes more than thirty years of nursing in neonatal intensive care units where she interacted with parents whose experiences were different from normal, natural births.[10] With a private practice of HT for families in Texas, she is currently on the advisory board of an NIH-funded project studying the effects of Healing Touch on critically ill infants. Rita writes, "In the beginning when HT started ... there were hints of caution because no one knew for sure how hands-on methods might affect a newborn baby. At first, I heeded the warnings, but situations … presented themselves that changed my outlook."

She continues, "One day, over ten years ago, a baby developed a clot in the femoral artery after a cardiac catheterization that was done to determine a congenital heart defect. The clot was significant; the leg showed signs of gangrene. Anticoagulant therapy was started, and I stepped up to the healing plate. The thought of an amputation of her leg made me abandon all caution, and I performed repetitive, short HT sessions. The baby's energy field felt like ice over her leg as if her life force was locally *frozen*. Long story short, even though the anticoagulants never affected her clotting times, the gangrene actually started to reverse itself within the next two days.

"Any hesitations to do the work were now gone. I was convinced of the efficacy of Healing Touch. We now know from experience that

HT treatments are most dramatic for acute conditions, first aid, and at the early onset of symptoms. These all have in common the fact that *there has not been enough time for the pattern to be [solidified]* ... The field is very malleable and responsive. I don't want to claim that every treatment is a miracle, because only nature and the Divine are in control of the healing."

As her experience with babies and families widened, Rita noted how the mother and child share a unified field, from conception through the first year of life. Recent research is showing that the template of this field, which influences the rest of the baby's life, is dependent on the physical, emotional, mental, and spiritual well-being of the mother. If the mother lives in constant tension and stress, she secretes stress hormones which cross the placental barrier into the baby's physiology, creating many adverse effects *before birth*.[11] Therefore, it is essential to educate a pregnant woman that her primary goal needs to be one of healthy self-care and respect for the future of the unborn child.

Rita often asks the mother-to-be to connect energetically by imaging a flow of energy from her heart to the unborn baby's heart with the goal of helping to start bonding as soon as woman is aware of the pregnancy. HT practitioners have many opportunities to influence the lives of families and friends by sharing this wisdom of taking time to send heart-centered caring to the forming child. Connecting energetically with love is the language all babies and children understand.

Rita is one of the pioneers in bringing energy healing to parents and babies and has made several important observations:

- Short treatments of approximately three to five minutes are desirable because the baby's field can respond rapidly.

- At critical times, longer treatments (up to twenty minutes) can help babies "turn the corner" faster, especially in cases like transit tachypnea (rapid heartbeat) of the newborn.

- Many times the HT effect is not immediate, but oxygen concentrations may increase significantly after a period of time or several sessions.

- Magnetic Passes and Magnetic Clearing are a great asset for helping an infant to recover from the anesthesia the mother receives via epidural or spinal administration.

- For babies with prematurity, congenital defects, and/or birth trauma, much can be done to minimize the negative effects of prolonged separation from the mother. Abrupt separation of the baby from its mother due to needed medical procedures or to adoption creates a tear in this unified field. A tear in the field causes a leak, an energetic drain on the entire human energy system. This drain in the biofield dampens the body's capacity to establish healthy immune function or to recover from trauma. Treatment to seal the baby's field in these instances can be helpful for minimizing the energetic impact of separation.

The field of the mother is also affected by separation. Technological methods to help stressed infants guarantee there will be much activity around the child. The mother often suffers extensive grief over fetal and infant distress, but her body and emotions frequently go unacknowledged in the hustle and bustle of hospital procedures. This presents a caregiving opportunity for every nurse or healthcare professional in neonatal settings. By creating time to listen to the mother's feelings and adding a HT method such as Magnetic Passes or Magnetic Clearing, the practitioner can contribute to the mother's healing at deeper levels, far beyond words.

Support for the Family Energy Field

Opportunities to work with the entire family in the perinatal and postnatal period abound, and we'll learn about HT classes for "expectant families" in the next chapter. Family life presents a multitude of challenges as each child achieves relevant developmental tasks with significant physical and psychological markers. It makes sense to assume there is a family energy field that can be strengthened with conscious efforts to bond such as described previously. Examples of the family energy field in action occur when members of a family have similar dreams or contact each other at the same moment when they are physically apart. "I was just thinking of you and then you called" is something emotionally close family members often say to each other.

The moment-by-moment dynamics of the family roller coaster can take the most focused and well-meaning parents by surprise. Parents may find themselves overwhelmed by a balky two-year-old, a child who indulges in temper tantrums, the unceasing activity levels of toddlers, the sassiness of a five-year-old learning to become an individual, the sulkiness of a child who does not like to go to school, the sadness of separation when a little friend moves away or a pet dies, or the hundreds of daily mini-crises that are part of family life. What is the most useful response? How can the parent stay centered while the child expresses his/her intense feelings? How can family friends, mentors, or grandparents help?

Work with energy healing concepts is becoming well defined in the maintenance of a healthy family. For example, the Magnetic Passes and other energetic releasing methods can be helpful in shaking off automatic emotions such as anger or helplessness when parents find themselves triggered by the energetic tension of daily family dramas.

Here's an exercise I have found helpful for such intense moments when a parent, grandparent, or caregiver must regroup in order to be fully present. It is impossible to attend to a child's emotions and needs when the adult is caught up in his/her own strong emotions. The exercise is written as if you, the reader, are the parent or helper, and undoubtedly you will see the ways you can use this approach.

Exercise 11.1. Acknowledging and Transforming a Negative Feeling

1. *Acknowledge as quickly as possible your strong feeling of irritation, tension, anger, or disappointment.*

2. *Place hands over the heart center to activate your sense of acceptance and forgiveness.*

3. *Add a self-affirming statement such as "Even though _____(name the specific incident) has happened/ or Even though I feel _____(name the feeling), I deeply and profoundly honor and accept myself." Repeat several times while gently massaging the heart chakra.*

4. *Think about your choices. Adults have the power to reflect, choose, and redirect their emotions. Children do not know how to do this. The way significant adults handle their emotions is quickly learned by children and may establish harmful lifelong patterns requiring later correction.*

5. *While continuing to hold or gently rub the heart area, affirm, "I choose to stay centered. I choose to try something helpful, and/or I choose to get more information and assistance."*

Although HT concepts cannot resolve all family dramas, especially more deeply ingrained patterns, teaching support for the family energy field can be a major boon to successful parenting. It is anticipated that the need for parenting classes will grow since our culture reflects unfortunate realities such as parent-child alienation, lack of an extended family or supportive community, and dispersion of families through divorce, frequent moving, and financial pressures.

HT for Building Personal Strengths in Adolescence

The developmental tasks of adolescence involve understanding and coping with major physical and emotional changes. Many children, especially those who go without the needed parental support to accomplish psychological maturing in the first decade of life, are at high risk to destructive outside influences that can lead to drug abuse, antisocial behaviors, or self-sabotaging sexual experiences.

The HT focus on centering and connecting with one's inner knowing can help teens to establish an *internal locus of control,* a sense of personal worth and self-esteem from within the person. HT practitioner and instructor Jeanette Nienabar is a science teacher in British Columbia who interweaves HT concepts with her high school science classes and is designing a course for adolescents offered through HTP. She writes: "When teaching, I've often found that a good metaphor for an abstract idea helps to facilitate student understanding. I was thinking of an appropriate metaphor for the teen program one day as I was watching some students texting with their cell phones. I realized that if they trusted the text they received from friends with no wires or cords connecting them, then this might be a useful metaphor for the idea of transferring energetic 'messages' to their body. The program theme 'Text Message Your Body' was born!

"The next task was to design an attractive and appropriate package using a combination of PowerPoint, activities, and Healing Touch techniques. I then set out to plan the implementation of the project and decided to include private treatments for staff and students, small group sessions in my resources classes, as well as several workshops in separate settings for students, parents, and staff."

Jeanette held the pilot program in the 2007–2008 school year and continued the next year while adding mini sessions on a Wellness Day and several "Stressbuster" presentations. Additionally, faculty and staff have experienced seventy-two documented full treatments since the fall of 2003.   Responses to the HT classes have been overwhelming from the students. A ninth grader writes: "[HT] helped me improve studying and working up to the honor roll level, which is my goal. My marks improved a lot as I worked with you. The Mind Clearing is another thing that I greatly appreciate. It helped me calm down and get my head straight in the worst times." Another calls HT "a great break from the rushed pace of student life." A very enterprising student describes HT thusly: "It helps cultivate an open mind and creates a great initiative! ... A mental change that can basically reboot your body."

A study that HT practitioner Pamela Potter Hughes initiated showed the impact of energetic techniques on teenagers in an adolescent psychiatric care unit.[12] These severely acting out teens reported increased feelings of self-worth within a few minutes of learning about centering and receiving interventions akin to Magnetic Passes. Repeated over time, the effects became even more marked and resulted in increased personal efficacy. Thinking things through and making better choices for themselves were the long-term outcomes the teens reported.

Niel Gilbert, who is both a psychiatric social worker and HT practitioner, has worked effectively with a number of adolescents to relieve their stressors, headaches, and other symptoms of adolescent identity struggles. He and others are pioneering in teaching energetic self-management to teens who crave independence, but much more needs to be done to bring adolescents' turbulent and scattered energies to an effective focus and strengthen personal esteem. As a young person learns to center himself and experience the unconditional caring of HT practitioners, transformation to self-acceptance and inner focus can occur.

HT in Drug Treatment Centers

Karl is director of a drug treatment facility on the East Coast. He recently attended a class in which he learned several HT methods. He was so impressed he asked the instructor, Lisa, to teach some of the self-mastery and self-esteem concepts to his patients. Very wisely, Lisa replied, "To really have an impact in your facility, I would like to teach you and your staff specific methods so the staff can teach your patients on a regular basis." This began exploration of a new course offering practical skills to assist patients in recovery from addictions that could be taught to interested members of Karl's staff.

Dora is a charge nurse in a drug treatment center on the West Coast. Her clients range from ages fifteen to sixty and often exhibit intense emotions, even suicidal ideation, as they detoxify and face the task of rebuilding their broken lives. After receiving the report from the previous shift, Dora asks all of the staff to center themselves for several minutes. Each staff member then shares practical ways they will help each other, especially with the clients on suicide watch. Over time, this simple exercise has built deep levels of cooperation and trust among the staff. The most difficult shifts flow well because the patients also sense the cohesiveness and supportive caring of the staff.

HT Resources for Midlife Challenges

What is popularly called "midlife crisis" is the time of life when a person realizes the clock is ticking, life is fleeting by, and one's great dream has not yet been accomplished. In fact, many people are so bogged down in adult life activities, careers, and families, they have lost track of their true selves and talents. Awakening to the need for personal fulfillment usually comes at ages ranging from forty to sixty. If the awakening occurs without guidance, hasty choices such as leaving one's family, divorcing, quitting a tedious job, or reliving adolescence may ensue, often with harmful consequences.

Fortunately, many HT practitioners are starting to see middle-aged clients with a stated need for focusing within, finding relief from external pressures, and considering future direction for their lives. Often, the internal processing of the client far exceeds the relaxation response so frequently reported. Practitioner Nancy Kalfallah shares the following story:

"On her second visit, [my middle-aged client] was extremely nervous about a math exam coming up the next day. I used the Chakra

Connection, Magnetic Clearing, and finished with Mind Clearing. During the Mind Clearing, my fingers had this 'stuck' sensation, so I decided to follow the energy and wait. After a [few] minutes, I became a little impatient so decided to close my eyes, ground myself, and relax. Within thirty to forty seconds, my whole field of vision became a stunning grass green and, shortly after, three white clouds entered this field of green. At that point, I decided to open my eyes and check on my client … She reported, 'My deceased mother, grandmother, and stepmother are all here. Mom and Grandma are each holding one of my hands and my stepmother has forgiven me for harsh words I spoke to her before she died. I then saw multiple generations of my deceased family members and all were happy together. They had all forgiven my father for being an alcoholic.' [The client] was extremely grateful for this life-changing experience because she had been feeling guilty for many years. She went on to complete her course of study, moved to more congenial surroundings, and began living more fully."

This is just one example of how a client's emotional life can shift positively when the practitioner allows the energy to move as needed to facilitate healing, which often takes an unexpected direction. This middle-aged client, for example, had no previous conscious awareness of the subconscious emotions and thoughts about the past that were creating a psychological burden for her.

Midlife is also a time when many people "drop out" or become discouraged with their lives. They may experience financial pressures related to long-term illnesses or bankruptcies. Others are simply underserved because they do not have strong educations or fit criteria for social services. HT practitioners like Janis Kleinberger choose to give back to their communities of vulnerable or underserved persons by offering sessions for little or low cost.

Healing Touch as a Companion to Healthy Aging

Energy Magazine, HT's monthly online magazine, recently high-lighted the growing presence of HT practitioners in senior communi-ties.[13] With more than 40 percent of the American population now over age fifty, public recognition is increasing about the issues and chal-lenges facing elders. HT practitioners are often part of new elder com-munities where they can readily share their insights and learnings. For example, Bernie Clarke, a fellow in nursing's highest honor, the Ameri-can Academy of Nursing, has been teaching HT for years in Panorama City, Washington, in the senior community where she lives. Sharing HT not only gives Bernie joy but also lends meaning to her full life at age eighty. It has also given Bernie a grateful and appreciative community, proving no one is too old to learn new life skills or to help others.

Another lively senior, HT practitioner and instructor Suzi Rhodes, of Laguna Woods Village, California, teaches senior residents while also being a performing member of the Aquadettes, a synchronized swimming organization. Practitioner Diana Hughes teaches at an elder center in Hemet, California, where she also serves as director of nurs-ing; and Barbara Dahl, HT practitioner and instructor for nearly twenty years, continues teaching her vibrant classes in Seattle, Washington. These are just a few examples of the many elders in the HT community who continue to thrive and derive joy from their sharing and service.

One might wonder if there is something about HT that fosters high-level wellness and longevity. Indeed, living with zest well beyond usu-al retirement age seems to be the norm rather than exception among those who are long-term members of the HT community. In addition to the frequent centering and bodily awareness taught in HT, we might also note that the very act of helping others generates endorphins and enhanced immune function.[14] Put simply, doing good is good for you.

End of Life Care

By far the most poignant and abundant stories about HT come from practitioners who have assisted clients with end of life care. Treatments may take place in hospitals, in homes, hospices, or palliative care facilities. Often, the importance of an intervention cannot be known until after the person's transition to the next life is completed and family members have time to reflect. In all cases, HT practitioners seem to be able to facilitate healing toward needed closure and peacefulness in the final stages of physical life.

Practitioner and instructor Cynthia Hutchison shares this story with deep appreciation and gratitude for the opportunity she had to facilitate a healing moment:

"John was a man in his thirties with AIDS and had been hospitalized for several weeks with worsening symptoms of his compromised immune system. What was most upsetting to his sister was his progressive dementia. I gave John one treatment at the city hospital where he was assigned a bed in a ward of men. We had never met previously. He was able to greet me and knew I was there to help. He closed his eyes after I began the treatment and remained asleep when I left an hour later. Chakra Connection was the opening method, followed by Chakra Spread. John's sister visited him the next day and reported he had no signs of dementia and they were able to go outside and share a beautiful day together. They talked with fun and humor, reminisced about their childhoods, expressed their love for each other, and spoke about his ensuing death. By the next day, John's dementia had returned and, about a month later, he died from complications of AIDS. John's sister spoke of the preciousness of that one day when John's mind and memories were clear enough for them to communicate. They came to closure with each other … Though John had no relief of physical symptoms, the single day of mental clarity provided a treasured opportunity. Both were then able to move on …"

As another example, practitioner Debbie Lundgren writes about her work in a hospice setting: "I work as a hospice nurse ... [and] receive referrals from the nurse case managers. I have seen numerous times how HT helps patients transition to the next life. It is especially useful for the agitation and anxiety that can be associated with the end of life. I was asked to see an elderly woman who was actively dying and very agitated. As I was working with her, she visibly relaxed. Her husband said it was the first time in days she looked comfortable. When I finished, I left the room for the two of them to be alone. When I returned, she had passed on. Her husband was [deeply] appreciative for the calmness [my intervention] had brought. I find incredible value doing HT for the end of life transition. Not only does the patient benefit, but so do the family and friends in the room."

Practitioner Judith Stoddard supported a client in his home setting through his final months of life and writes: "At age sixty-six, Bruno was diagnosed with pancreatic and liver cancer and given three months to live. He felt he put himself into the hands of God through my hands. During HT sessions, Bruno felt energy, relaxed deeply, and saw varying shades and patterns of colors. Our intentions were to strengthen his immune system, increase efficacy of chemotherapy while decreasing side effects, and [facilitate] healing for his highest good. Until his last moments, he lived an active life with minimal chemotherapy side effects and effective pain management ... His incomparable gift was the opportunity for me to learn what 'heart-centered' truly means: *feeling* love and compassion pouring out of my heart center into another person while doing Healing Touch. And for that gift, I will be forever thankful."

In reading these stories, we become aware of the twofold gift of HT as a deepening spiritual practice. Clients receive the experience of needed clarity or peacefulness while caregivers experience their own appreciation of the mystery of life and its further evolution beyond the physical body.

We've explored how the Healing Touch presence changes the lives of the people it reaches and how it can be applied at any stage of the life cycle. Because of the resourcefulness and creativity within the HT community, new courses in addition to the five-level core curriculum have been set up to serve specific populations. In the next chapter, we will consider some of these expanded applications.

Chapter Notes

1. H. Out, J. Dusek, T. Liberman, et al., "Genomic counter-stress changes induced by the relaxation response," www.Plos ONE.com; retrieved July 26, 2008.

2. R. McCraty, M. Atkinson, and D. Tomasino, "Modulation of DNA conformation by heart-focused intention" (Boulder Creek, CA: Institute of HeartMath, 2003).

3. J. Mentgen, personal communication during a Level One HT class in 1998.

4. B. Brennan, *Hands of Light* (New York: Bantam, 1988), 67–68.

5. D. Hover-Kramer, *Second Chance at Your Dream: Engaging your body's energy resources for optimal aging, creativity, and health* (Santa Rosa, CA: Energy Psychology Press, 2009), 72–73.

6. E. H. Erikson, *Identity and the Life Cycle* (New York: W.W. Norton, 1959).

7. A. Judith, *Waking the Global Heart: Humanity's rite of passage from the love of power to the power of love* (Santa Rosa, CA: Elite Books, 2006).

8. E. H. Erikson, *The Life Cycle Completed* (New York: W.W. Norton, 1998).

9. Hover-Kramer, *op. cit.*, 73.

10. R. Kluny, personal communications April 20- 30, 2009; see also her website www.healingtouchforbabies.com.

11. W. A. McCarty, *Welcoming Consciousness* (Santa Barbara, CA: WB Publishing, 2009), see also her website www.wondrousbeginnings. com; D. Chamberlain, *The Mind of Your Newborn Baby* (Berkeley, CA: North Atlantic Books, 1998).

12. P. P. Hughes, R. Meize-Grochowski, and C. N. Harris, "Therapeutic Touch with psychiatric adolescent patients," *Journal of Holistic Nursing* 14(1997): 6–23.

13. *Energy Magazine* 33 (April 2009), issue focusing on HT with elders; accessed through www.energymagazineonline.com.

14. C. Wallis, "The new science of happiness," *Time* (January 15, 2005).

Chapter 12
Expanded Roles for Healing Touch Practitioners

If you know energy, you need to know structure. If you know structure, you need to know energy. If you know both, you need to know how to put them together.

—Fritz Smith, MD

Because of HT's broad applications for assisting people in need, many Healing Touch practitioners have expanded their practices to include new and innovative applications. They are artists putting two or more concepts together in creative ways as suggested in the opening quote. The questing curiosity of many practitioners leads them to want more information as they find new applications for HT. They also want to follow their interests and learning needs. It is apparent that many practitioners come alive to themselves through their work with energy methods and develop a seemingly insatiable appetite for further knowledge!

In response to requests from these creative practitioners, a number of specialty courses have been or are in the process of being developed within HTP. Offered through HTP and listed each month in Energy Magazine,[1] they include the following:

- **HT Advanced Practice:** Level 1 & 2 courses to deepen understanding of HT practice, new full-body methods, sacred geometry, and trauma release interventions.

- **HT Level 6:** The course for training HT instructors, offered in the United States, Canada, and Europe on a regular basis, and other nations as requested.

- **Therapeutic Communication in HT:** With emphasis on principles for effective listening and reaching complex client populations, taught by nurse psychotherapist Sharon Scandrett-Hibdon and psychotherapist Donna Donato.

- **HT Self-care:** Taught by trained HT instructors; described in detail in the next chapter.

- **My Helpful Healing Touch:** A book [2] and course for empowering children in the basic principles of energy healing.

- **HT for Adolescents (in the process of being developed):** A new course being designed introducing HT and the concepts of energy medicine to teens.

- **HT in Long-term Care and Nursing Homes (in the process of being developed):** This course will offer the elderly methods to aid in self care enhancing their well being.

- **HT in the Home:** HTP is in the process writing a book with this title for the general population about energetic first aid for the home. It will include a table of first aid with specific HT methods.

- **HT Trauma Release:** A course in the process of being developed to introduce an energetic approach to working with trauma called the Trauma Release Technique. As originally envisioned by Janet Mentgen, this powerful technique provides relief to clients who are experiencing long-term effects from a traumatic event.

Instructor Kathy Allen explains the Trauma Release: "Scientific research into the neurophysiology of trauma reveals that our primary response [to trauma] is instinctive and biological while our secondary response is psychological and cognitive.[3] Our bodies have already prepared to take action (fight or flight) ... before we are even consciously aware of it. If we are thwarted from being able to take action, this survival energy remains trapped in our systems where it can lead to the development of physical and emotional symptoms as well as to destructive behaviors ... When used in the context of trauma ... internal cues [held] in the body may lead to the spontaneous return of the traumatic stress state.[4] For example, the sight of a Humvee may activate internal cues for trauma in a war veteran and return him to his original stressed state. The sound of a siren may activate internal cues for accident survivors and put them into traumatic stress. The goal of the Trauma Release Technique is to extinguish these internal cues and to stop the perpetuation of the trauma response.

"As an example, John was flying home from a business trip when passengers were told that the landing gear was stuck and they should prepare for a crash landing. The flight attendant's face was tense and fearful as she gave the passengers instructions on how to brace themselves. John could see the fire engines on the runway 'standing by to clean up the mess.' At the last minute, the landing gear dropped down and the plane landed safely. John was scheduled to fly the next weekend for another business trip so he came to see me right away to reduce his anxiety.

"I adjusted the Trauma Release Technique to treat John's shock and recent trauma. During the treatment, John felt a strong urge to run so I told him to use his imagination and see himself running. He had a spontaneous image of himself sliding down the yellow emergency chute and running away from the burning plane as he held the hand of a child who had been seated next to him. As we continued to work, the image returned and this time he saw himself slide down the emergency chute and run away from the plane with all of his might ... he ran until he felt safe. John was able to use imagery to complete what his nervous system had instinctually prepared him to do if the plane crashed. The Trauma Release Technique extinguished the somatic cues of trauma in his body and he was able to fly the following weekend without any discomfort."

Kathy concludes, "Trauma is a fact of life, but it does not have to be a life sentence. Whether the traumatic experience occurred recently or in the distant past, it is possible to recover from it and to reclaim the fullness of life."

International Outreach of Healing Touch

We now briefly review HT's international outreach in selected countries. This outreach demonstrates another expanded role of HT practitioners and instructors. Those teaching in other countries demonstrate their flexibility by bridging from the basic HT curriculum to the specific interests and needs of each different cultural environment. Many also struggle with finding the best way to name and express energy-related terms in a foreign language.

Canada

Practitioner and instructor Kathy Layte shares, "Healing Touch started in Canada in 1994 in Toronto, Ontario. From these humble beginnings, Healing Touch classes from Levels One through Five spread quickly and have been taught from the west coast of British Columbia to the east coast of Newfoundland. There are large active communities of practitioners in major centers across the country and in small, more remote areas serving persons from all backgrounds and walks of life including First Nation communities. Many healthcare centers and schools have actively embraced Healing Touch as a comforting and supportive modality for those they serve.

"The Healing Touch Association of Canada was formed soon after classes began. Its mission is to encourage the spread Healing Touch in communities across Canada. This group sponsors a biannual conference attended by more than one hundred practitioners and instructors from across the country. It also publishes a Canadian newsletter called Nexus and provides member support through advocacy, education, and support of one's practice wherever needed. The Canadian Healing Touch Foundation was established in the mid-1990s as a charitable organization which continues to receive and distribute funds to advance Healing Touch in Canada."

Germany/Europe

Practitioner and instructor Ines Hoster had a burning desire to bring HT to her birth country, Germany. She started by purchasing two copies of the first HT textbooks to share with her German friends on her visit there in 1997. She offered several pilot workshops on her next visit. Once the interest was kindled, she offered a Level One class in 1998. Since then she has taught more than sixty classes and has sought translators for significant portions of the HT manuals. She continues to plan international European conferences that include participants from Italy, Austria, Switzerland, Holland, and the Netherlands. Ines also teaches HT courses in Switzerland and Italy.[5] About 1,500 students have attended one or more classes; fifteen practitioners are now certified and three instructors are in training. Notably, Ines' untiring efforts brought about the first full five-level trainings in a non–English speaking country. Translation of the course material and this book is now being planned.

Finland

HT outreach in Finland is spearheaded by Finn-born Rauni King who has been teaching classes there on her annual visits since 1999. Recently, a Level Five class held the first graduation ceremonies.[6]

South Africa

HT outreach has begun in the Zulu communities of South Africa with a strong response from a people who have honored shamanic healing traditions for thousands of years. [7]

Australia

Mary Jo Bulbrook began HT classes in Perth, Australia, on her sabbatical there in 1993. Since then, more than a thousand people have taken at least one level of HT coursework and an active community of practitioners and instructors networks throughout that vast country.[8]

Peru

One of the fastest growing areas for HT development is Peru where numerous classes and networks have been established under the leadership of an active Board.[9]

The Netherlands

Wietzke van Oone writes, "Our organization is called 'Stichting Healing Touch Nederland,' which means 'Healing Touch Netherlands Foundation,' and was founded in June 1996. We are a nonprofit foundation with a minimum of three board members, and we are registered (for tax purposes) in the Netherlands. We have had from 1996 to 2008 approximately seven hundred students studying Healing Touch."[10]

Mexico

Connie Silva reports, "I teach mainly in Mexico through the university system and mostly the school of nursing. People of different disciplines, including traditional healers and psychics, embrace HT. As of two years ago, there was one master's level study of HT completed, on depression on patients with mastectomies due to breast cancer. There is another one going on with psychiatric nurses to study burnout in the care of outpatients. People use and do HT in many settings, helping children in orphanages, students of nursing, and clients with chronic illness. I have taught two Level Four classes and am getting ready for a Level Five."[11]

Japan

Sarah Porter, lives in Hawaii and teaches in Japan, and says, "Since 2004, we have conducted numerous introductory workshops. Since 2007, we've held three Level One classes and two of Level Two. We will offer each of levels one through three [at least] once a year."[12] She is also interested in translating some of the HT manuals into Japanese.

Related Course Offerings Allied to HT

In addition to this rich variety of offerings for those who love to advance their HT comprehension, there are several other programs that were developed under independent leadership rather than through HTP auspices. These courses reach many energy therapy practitioners and are often featured at HT and other national conferences. Class schedules are given through HT's monthly communication channel, the *Energy Magazine*. These independent programs, which are aligned with HT, include:

- **Touching Body, Tending Soul: Spiritual Dimensions of Healing Practice:** A new telecourse developed by Janet Quinn, PhD, RN, FAAN.

- **Physics and Spiritual Healing for Healers:** Developed by Vicki Slater, PhD, RN, HTCP/I.

- **Anatomy and Physiology for Healers:** Developed by Sue Hovland, MS, RN HTCP/I.

- **Healing Touch for Animals (HTA):** developed by Carol Komitor, BSN, RN, HTCP/I.

- **Healing Touch Spiritual Ministry (HTSM):** Developed by Linda Smith, RN, HTCP/I.

- **Healing Touch for Babies:** Developed by Rita Kluny, RN, HTCP/I.

We'll now explore some of these programs more fully.

Anatomy and Physiology for Healers

Sue Hovland started practicing and teaching HT in 1990 and became certified as a practitioner and instructor in 1993. She explains that her "passion for learning healing led me to expand my background in nursing, anatomy, and Healing Touch by going to massage school, studying neuromuscular therapy, cranial-sacral therapy, visceral and lymph massage, human dissection, energetic allergy release, Axiatonal Alignment, and aromatherapy. All of this brought a deepening knowledge of the miracle of the human body and energy system; [it kindled] my desire to share that information.

"This led to the birth of the Anatomy for Healers Program[13] with a workshop offered in 1997. It's an accumulation of knowledge I've learned from my anatomy studies, past and continuing, my HT foundational courses, and further energy medicine studies. The more I really understand anatomy, the more my clients are releasing quickly and deeply, and the more specific is my guidance.

"The Healing Touch Program continues to be supportive of the Anatomy for Healers program, giving CE credits for nurses and massage therapists. The courses I offer are an independent advanced study for experienced healers who have completed Level Three of the HT program or have equivalent backgrounds. The workshops enhance [HT studies] by learning and applying anatomy insights. This approach has helped students do deeper, more specific, and effective work. Nurses and others who have studied anatomy before also find it valuable, because traditional anatomy [courses don't] integrate energy aspects with the physical body.

"Getting acquainted energetically with the cardiovascular system, for example, is a profound experience, and the energy field in the classroom pulses with the etheric heartbeat. Students are amazed at how they can actually energetically feel the difference between the liver, stomach, pancreas, intestines, kidneys, and so on … former students will tell me that they use the knowledge all the time, and find it was one of the most valuable workshops they have ever taken."

Healing Touch Spiritual Ministry

Linda L. Smith, president of the Healing touch Spiritual Ministry and the Institute of Spiritual Healing and Aromatherapy,[14] describes her independent program with great enthusiasm:"As Healing Touch began to grow throughout the world, it was only natural for it to be recognized as a form of spiritual healing. Some people described this newfound knowledge as something they had always 'known,' as if it were bubbling up through their ancestral roots or embedded in their DNA. They found themselves tapping into spiritual knowing that resulted in positive life changes both for themselves and their loved ones.

"Some, in their enthusiasm, began to teach Healing Touch techniques in their churches, synagogues, and various spiritual circles with varying degrees of success. There were others who were drawn to the work but struggled to see how Healing Touch matched their spiritual beliefs. Still others wanted to know how to explain energy healing to their ministers or priests without being accused of practicing witchcraft... A few even feared they would be excommunicated for practicing healing.

"In 1997, Janet Mentgen gave me the opportunity to start a new program called the Healing Touch Spiritual Ministry (HTSM) program to address these spiritual issues and to provide direction for bringing Healing Touch formally into all denominations of Christian churches.

The approach includes three forms of vibrational healing:

- Prayer
- Hands-on or energy healing
- Anointing with essential oils

"These three forms of healing were often demonstrated by Jesus and taught in the early church. Clearly, Jesus was a masterful healer and knew when 'power' [the Greek word is energeia] went out from him.[15] Healing was primary in his ministry and was so important that he sent his disciples out into the towns and villages to heal and anoint all who were ill. He gave them practical experiences so that when he left them, they would know what to do.[16]

"The early Christians continued Jesus' model of healing and became phenomenal healers as attested to in the Acts of the Apostles.[17] What made them so successful? I believe they tapped into [the] three forms of vibrational healing, only they did not have the language to describe this phenomenon. They prayed, laid on hands, and anointed with oil all who were sick.[18] They continued this form of healing for hundreds of years until power and politics began to set down 'rules' as to who could heal and under what circumstances one could receive healing.

"Over time, healing became one of the church's sacramental rituals, like baptism and penance; anointing was reserved for the last moment of life to assist the soul, not for everyday healing. Healing thus fell out of Christianity nearly five hundred years ago, not to begin a return until our present day.

"The vision of Healing Touch Spiritual Ministry is to restore healing to Christianity, as most Christians have lost sight of the central role it was meant to have. From our very beginning, the HTSM program has offered continuing education for both nurses and massage therapists. Courses have been taught throughout the United States, Canada, Trinidad / Tobago, Italy, South Africa, and India—wherever we are invited to teach. A code of ethics and standards of practice direct our practice."

Linda concludes, "HTSM has developed over these past twelve years into a certification program similar in construction to the Healing Touch Program. HTSM graduates uses the HTP certification vehicle for its own certification processes. After learning about the history of healing in the church and becoming comfortable with the concepts, students learn in a stepped fashion to complete our basic program of instruction. An in-depth student manual is used for each course. Other allied courses continue to be developed."

Douglas L. Suggs, chaplain at the Arbor Acres United Methodist Senior Residential Center, reported a recent study done in a clinic where HTSM practitioners provided healing intervention to community elders.[19] He states, "Individually, the study indicates that HTSM is good for our residents, providing many positive holistic benefits, thus contributing to their overall quality of life ... such as relief of physical pain, stress relief, better sleep, a sense of peace, receiving love, relief from depression, and so on ... The implications are clear that if HTSM is this helpful for the residents of the study, then it should benefit any [senior] willing to include it as a part of their care regimen. Outside of providing relief from specific health issues, the study also indicates that HTSM is good for general health maintenance. As one ages, there can be a loss of control over personal care, a sense of helplessness, and chronic conditions that do not improve with traditional treatments, resulting in dependency and loss of dignity. HTSM gives residents a way to do something to benefit themselves, thus furthering their sense of self-esteem and health."

Pastor Suggs continues, "The study also has implications for individuals and organizations who are interested in preventive care and complementary therapies, given the rising cost of healthcare. Many people are seeking ways to grow in their spirituality, with an interest in healing ministries. This study will contribute to the longer-range goal of the chaplaincy department to develop a model of HTSM for other retirement communities, caregiver organizations, and churches, as incentive to start their own programs. Finally, it contributes, in a small way, to the growing movement to renew the church in reclaiming its ministries of healing."

Healing Touch for Babies

One of the sad realities of the twenty-first century is that many women do not take time to let pregnancy be an opportunity for self-nurturing and joy. Pregnancy is a sacred time, which needs to be honored by the whole family surrounding the unborn child. This "expectant family," including the father and close family relatives, can learn to bond by strengthening their heart-to-heart energetic connections with each other and the forming baby.

Rita Kluny regularly offers classes for parents, professionals, and caregivers as part of her Healing Touch for Babies program established in 2000.[20] She invites participants with, "Come learn how to hold your baby's heart ... Learn ... the best way to communicate with your unborn child!" The weekend workshop contents include basic principles of energy healing, the development of consciousness during gestation, research from prenatal and perinatal psychology, and specific ways to enhance emotional and physical well-being for all concerned. Her emphasis is to help caregivers learn to treat the infant with safety, respect, and understanding. Rita has found HT can also minimize stress during the birth process and speed recovery, while at the same time deepening family bonds with the newborn.

Rita understands that parents are the barometer, or indicator, for their baby's experience of emotional safety. In other words, if the parents are calm and centered, the baby experiences a sense of peace; on the other hand, if the parents are anxious or fighting, the child's field is disrupted and fussing and crying ensue. The state of the parents' energy field thus greatly influences child development. Rita sums up her wisdom from her many years of experience with HT in her forthcoming book, *Holding Your Baby's Heart.*

Healing Touch for Animals

Healing Touch for Animals (HTA) is an energy healing modality that assists animals by supporting their self-healing. It teaches a curriculum of energy techniques that address the inner workings of animals' energy systems and provide a stable healing environment within a secure animal-human bond.[21] HTA was developed by massage therapist and veterinary technician Carol Komitor, HTCP/I, who understood the difference in animals' energy systems as compared to that of humans. She was encouraged by animal-appreciator Janet Mentgen, HTP founder. Carol created all HTA techniques to help human practitioners choose the correct animal energy medicine applications.

Carol explains, "First recognition of how people did not understand the inner workings of an animal's energy system came when I received frequent questions from the Healing Touch Program office. Some people were practicing HT on their animals for various conditions and either saw the animal run away or were puzzled about ways to begin helping their beloved pets. Human practitioners were frustrated, confused, and perplexed as to why the effective HT energy techniques they used with human clients were not accepted by animals.

"After several pilot classes, the first HTA Workshop, a full weekend experience, was taught in 1996. HTA quickly developed into a multi-levelprogram that builds on concepts of the animal's energy system and provides numerous healing techniques, aromatherapy, and sound therapy ... I found the methods helped the human pet owners as well! The HTA Program leads to certification giving practitioners the qualifications, knowledge, and professionalism to be a competent healthcare provider for animals. Many veterinary professionals are integrating HTA into their practices as they provide energy medicine treatments. They blend necessary traditional medical services with those of holistic healthcare to accelerate the well-being of animals and provide the very best in veterinary healthcare.

"The basic concept is that animals have a much more expanded and sensitive energy system than humans. They utilize their life-force energy with all aspects of their presence, 24/7, which maximizes their instinctual abilities. In general, animals have an energy field that is ten or more times greater than that of humans. The energy field around their bodies helps them monitor their surroundings for safety from predation and ensure their comfort level."

From Carol's experience, the energy system of animals is similar to that of humans but is accessed differently. She continues, "The animal's energetic matrix has seven main chakras, minor chakras at each joint of the body, minor chakras at each organ, and a group of minor chakras that work with the spiritual and instinctual sense of their beings. Just as with humans, animal energy will release congestion and create an energetic environment for self-healing. The amazing thing about animals is that their self-healing capacity initiates and sets the stage for quick healing. Whether the animal is a domestic pet, an animal that is connected to a herd, or an animal in the wild, they accept the workings of their energy system as an interactive matrix to function."

Carol and her practitioner groups find animals accept Healing Touch for Animals with little resistance. Animals instinctively sense that the practitioner is providing them with healing. They activate their own relaxation responses to set in motion natural physiological functions for self-healing. Relaxation provides a release of a variety of endorphins that start the domino effect to support all parts of their bodies. Physical issues, emotional upsets, and mental stress can be relieved with the work of HTA. There are specific techniques that address illness, inappropriate behavior, self-esteem and confidence levels, the animal-human bond, respite/hospice care, and support through euthanasia and death.

Carol concludes, "Practitioners of HTA are now supporting animal populations around the world. They are helping animals in their homes, through their private practices, in veterinary facilities, and in animal shelters. HTA practitioners also utilize positive applications by working with zookeepers and in animal competition settings. Energy medicine with HTA gives practitioners well-rounded applications to help animals and their people."

HT's Interface with the Practice of Psychotherapy

As a nurse, counselor, and psychologist, my own energy therapy practice grew during the ten years I taught HT around the nation from 1989 to 1999. I then cofounded the Association for Comprehensive Energy Psychology (ACEP) to support psychotherapists interested in energy therapies.[22] Like many other HT practitioners specializing in counseling, the underlying energetic concepts of HT are a integral part of my practice. These core concepts are also visible in many components of ACEP's certification programs, which integrate biofield, chakra, and meridian interventions.

My evolution to developing ACEP was actually inspired by a group of psychologists from San Diego, California, who had attended various HT classes. They started asking me questions about applying energy concepts in their therapeutic practices. Together we explored this interface with specialized seminars over three years. This set the stage for the formation of the new association that I cofounded in 1999 with David Gruder, PhD. By 2009, ACEP counted more than one thousand members and has outreach in nearly thirty countries.

As we have seen in many of the HT reports, clients experience both physical and emotional relief with HT. In addition, many have received new insights and ideas and a sense of connection to the Higher Self, the transpersonal consciousness. Body, mind, and spirit are affected by energy interventions and thus provide a unique resource for health caregivers in helping clients to go beyond words to the deeper levels required for releasing trauma and building self-esteem.

Chapter Notes

1. HTP's *Energy Magazine;* to register and receive your free copy, go online to www.EnergyMagazineOnline.com.

2. *My Helpful Healing Touch: A guide for empowering children* is published by Healing Touch Program (San Antonio, TX) and teaches energetic principles to children.

3. P. A. Levine, *Waking the Tiger: Healing trauma* (Berkeley, CA: North Atlantic Books, 1997).

4. R. C. Scaer, *The Trauma Spectrum: Hidden wounds and human resiliency* (New York: W.W. Norton, 2005). Also see "The role of energy in healing trauma," Energy Magazine (February 2007); www.HealingTouch-Program.com.

5. See *Energy Magazine* (July 2008) for description of HT programs and recent developments in Germany and northern Italy, South Africa, Australia, and Finland by going to the archived issues link: http://www.energymagazineonline.com/energey_archived_issues/july2008.pdf

6. *Ibid.*

7. *Ibid.*

8. *Ibid.*

9. Organization in Peru as reported in May 2009 issue of Energy Magazine.

10. Address: Lange Lakenstraat 17, postal code 2011 ZB City; Haarlem www.healingtouch.nl; e-mail: info@healingtouch.nl.

11. Personal communication, May 2009. Connie Silva's e-mail: subtle-energies @sbsglobal.net.

12. Personal communication, May 2009. Sarah Porter's e-mail: sereporterslcn@hotmail.com.

13. Personal communication, May 2009. For more information, please visit www.anatomyforhealers.com.

14. L. Smith, personal communication, May 2009. Contact information: http://www.ISHAhealing.com; e-mail: Staff@ISHAhealing.com; phone: 303-467-7829.

15. *The Holy Bible.* Luke 8:46.

16. *Ibid.*, Mark 6:7–13. Also see Luke 10:1,10.

17. *Ibid.*, Acts 2:43,47.

18. *Ibid.*, James 5:14–16.

19. Personal communication with Douglas L. Suggs reporting on the Arbor Acres project evaluation, May 2009; e-mail: dsuggs@arboracres.org; phone: 336-748-4645.

20. R. Kluny, founder Healing Touch for Babies. Contact information: 3605 Steck Avenue, Suite 1105, Austin, TX 78759, website: www.healingtouchfor babies.com.

21. Website: www.healingtouchforanimals.

22. Association for Comprehensive Energy Psychology (ACEP); www.energypsych.org.

Section IV

Ongoing Development of the Healing Touch Practitioner

Chapter 13
Self-care and Personal Development of the Practitioner

When I am clear, everything else is also more clear.

—HT student

Challenges of Being a Caregiver

It is a special challenge to all of us blessed with a humanistic ethic to give quality care beyond mere distribution of medication or administration of technical treatments. In our efforts to lead with compassion and empathy, we may actually lose ourselves. In other words, we may become so oriented toward the requirements of others that we forget our own needs.

The roots of nursing are especially strong in total dedication for others because of the alignment of nursing with the religious traditions of Europe. For hundreds of years prior to Florence Nightingale's enlightened view of nurses as emancipated healers who could create healing environments for their patients,[1] caregivers were mostly convent nuns who served without pay. Caregivers were also kindhearted, though often sloppy "women of ill repute" like the famed Dickens character Sarie Gamp, who further downgraded society's valuing of the helper role. Happily, caregivers have come a long way since then to augment the status of healthcare professionals and receive more adequate pay and recognition. However, many family caregivers who are often lay-persons still struggle to be recognized as being of worth to their families and society at large.

Thinking about the emotional, mental, and spiritual needs of caregiving practitioners is still in its infancy. Burnout, a state of mind in which the caregiver becomes indifferent to his/her profession or too overwhelmed to function effectively, occurs much too frequently. It is estimated, for example, that current nursing shortages in most states are less related to an actual lack of new graduates and more likely caused by sheer exhaustion. Many flee from the nursing profession to find new careers.[2] Retention in nursing is low since many of its most creative minds move on to other disciplines that are less emotionally taxing.

The prevalence of burnout among caregivers may be due to the outgoing, overly altruistic idealism of many caregivers. In addition, caregivers often exhibit an internal dynamic of self-depreciation with tendencies to avoid attention to personal needs.

To complicate matters, many healthcare professionals are engaged not only in trying to give quality care in clinical settings but also in taking care of family members. Besides raising children or being available to their adult children, a large percentage of caregivers also engage in meeting the practical needs of one or more elderly parents. This dynamic is currently estimated to affect one out of four American households. So prevalent is this dilemma, it is called the "sandwich generation," referring to those who have caregiving responsibilities at both ends of their own midlife years. Women are a significantly larger proportion of such family caregivers and often fill multiple roles of mother, wife, healthcare professional, and ad hoc medical helper for an older person. A recent study estimates that over 8.7 million women are members of the sandwich generation; these women are at risk for twice the usual number of chronic conditions and can have a shortened life span by up to ten years.[3]

Many caregivers are indeed wounded healers. They may live on a treadmill of hoping someone will take care of them equally as well as they try to take care of others. This expectation is called the "Please Me" driver, meaning, "I will do everything I can to please you so you will then please me, in turn." It is described as a driving psychological motivator in Transactional Analysis [4] and is often coupled with a "Try Harder" driver, that is, "If pleasing others does not work, I will simply try harder." The expectations of persons with "Please Me/Try Harder" drivers are unfortunately seldom met. Over and over, kindly people are disappointed when other people do not reciprocate as desired.

Stress in the workplace unquestionably takes its toll on healthcare professionals. But recipients of care also pay a price. Iatrogenic disease caused by medical treatments and illnesses due to being in a hospital while exposed to inadequate care affects more than a third of all patients. Medical errors are a leading cause of death in this country—higher than motor vehicle accidents, breast cancer, or AIDS.[5] Put another way, overly stressed or less than conscious caregivers may actually cause more harm than good.

These alarming statistics demand that caregivers pay attention to themselves. Personal self-care is the best antidote to the downward pull of being overwhelmed by the unending tasks facing caregivers. Since one of the guiding principles of Healing Touch is personal centering before entering into the patient's field, HT practitioners already have one built-in pathway for personal care. Other components of self-care (presented in brief here) must follow to prevent burnout and bring ongoing vitality to healing endeavors.

Principles and Limitations of Self-care

Energy-oriented interventions always begin with the focused

intention of the caregiver. Moreover, this intention is aligned with the unlimited supply of energy from the Universal Energy Field. Establishing this connection and trusting it fully means practitioners are energized rather than depleted when giving treatments. True healing flows from this Source to the practitioner who, in turn, receives its blessings. When the caregiver is filled with energy, resources for balancing the client's field can then be shared.

Knowing yourself and your needs is thus a central ethic in caregiving. Others, least of all you, cannot be enriched from emptiness. If your biofield is compromised, or you are "under the weather" or "not quite up to snuff," do not attempt to serve others, especially in a private practice. The best move is to rest, nurture the body with good nutrition, healthy fluids, and supplements, and sort out emotional stressors that may be impacting your optimal functioning. Rest assured, everyone will appreciate you caring enough to keep your depleted field to yourself!

As caregivers become increasingly attuned to the direct messages from the body, they learn to respond more quickly and prevent onset or severity of opportunistic illness such as the flu. Here are four major ways to enhance immune system function through personal awareness:

1. **When you're tired, rest!** The body knows what it needs and is trying its best to communicate its needs. Let go of all your real or imagined duties, pare them down to bare essentials and get off your feet. Even a thirty-minute "power nap" can be the rejuvenation your immune system needs.

2. **Eat well at least three times a day and take time to enjoy your food!** Proteins are the cellular fuels. Fresh fruits and veggies rebuild tissue. Avoid carbohydrates, especially the empty-calorie ones which are mostly sugars and result in a short burst of seeming energy while depleting your insulin supply. Stay away from carbonated drinks.

3. **Exercise in moderation** by doing some aerobic movement each day to stay fit and stimulate endorphin production, which also supports immune function.

4. **Repeat positive self-affirming statements** such as, "Even though I have a lot on my plate, I choose to listen to my body and to nurture my immune system … I deserve to be well and stay healthy … I release my fears … There is no room for illness in my energy body."

Being so grounded in reality may sound selfish or self-centered to people who are overzealous about the helping role. There is nothing glamorous, however, about being a wounded helper and, from the wounding, passing on one's dysfunctions to others. Enlightenment requires dedication to rigorous self-knowledge and willingness to be a sensitive role model of personal self-caring.

Most of us do not become enlightened without assistance. One of the reasons mentoring by an experienced practitioner is built into the HT program is to assist apprentices to look at their personal issues. Referrals to more specialized counseling resources are also strongly encouraged in the HT program to bolster inner strengths.

There are decidedly limitations to self-care such as a powerful emotional upsets, either past or present, which cannot be released readily. It is appropriate and essential to seek professional help for personal issues. Just in time for such challenges, a large number of practicing psychotherapists with special skills in energy therapies are now available. They can rapidly and effectively facilitate inner work for releasing deep-seated problems and patterns. (For access to such therapists, see the ACEP contact information in appendix E.)

Healing Touch Self-care

Daily self-care with the methods of HT is a boon to practitioners. Most HT methods described earlier can be modified for use in self-care. Here we explore some of them as transformed into personal care exercises.

Certified HT practitioner Barbara Starke takes personal self-care of the healer to another level with a one-day course dedicated to caring for the HT caregiver. In this workshop she teaches basic HTP techniques with an emphasis on clearing and balancing the field of the individual practitioners and instructors. This course also includes other significant basics of self-care: artistic expression through color and drawing, the use of positive self-talk, and the value of self-knowledge though journaling. About conventional healthcare settings, she writes, "Practitioners are forced by the current system to treat symptoms with tools that merely gloss over the underlying imbalances and do not honor the relationship physical ailments have to the mind-body-spirit connection." Increasing emphasis on cost containment, measurable outcomes, and strict medical protocols leave little time for the human touch of caring consciousness. The discrepancy between real human needs and high-tech pressures in current conventional care puts many caregivers in a push-and-pull dilemma of great emotional distress."

Barbara continues, "Healing Touch exemplifies what Jean Watson speaks of as the Caring Moment[6] ... of creating a conscious awareness of our shared humanity. There's no way to accomplish this without starting with the Self ... from my Soul to another's Soul. I wish to practice being Present to my own inner nature [first]."

Centering as the Foremost Ethic

In my book about ethics for energy therapists, *Creating Right Relationships*, I speak of centering as the caregiver's most basic ethic.[7]

We cannot in good conscience interact with another person's energy field, chakras, or meridians without being connected to our Higher Self and its Source. Hundreds of paths to a peaceful sense of self include the many approaches to focused breathing, various forms of visual imagery, and repetition of poems, mantras, or affirmations. Being fully present to oneself allows creativity to flow. New interests, answers from the inner advisor and guidance can then emerge with ease and joy.

Chakra Meditation

Because of the psychodynamic nature of the chakras, they offer an excellent template for personal development. Each chakra has its own unique contribution and energy for the whole of your being.

Here's one meditation I use almost daily to uplift my energies while allowing the hands to rest or spin over each of the seven major chakras.

Exercise 13.1. Meditation Through the Chakras

Root chakra: "*I sense my being, my roots into the earth. I am safe and secure in the hands of peace.*"

Sacral chakra: "*I accept my feelings as helpful friends. I note what attracts me and readily choose to release what does not fit.*"

Solar Plexus: "*I honor my power, my ability to think and speak with clarity. I release any demands of others.*"

Heart chakra: "*I honor and accept myself. I let go of grudges easily and accept others as they are.*"

Throat chakra: "*I enjoy my creativity. My joy lies in finding and sharing truth without judgment.*"

Brow chakra: "*I see with insight and compassion. Wisdom guides me to perceive with accuracy.*"

Crown chakra: "*I open to the Creator of All with enthusiasm. I sense my path to the Light.*"

This meditation can be done in the shower or near a body of water to potentiate its power. Music and quiet time for writing down your thoughts and insights are also fine ways to maximize the effects of this meditation.

The Self Chakra Connection

The Chakra Connection, as described in chapter 6, can be modified to be a powerful self-help resource. Other excellent sources for self-care methods are adapting the Opening Spiral (chapter 7) and the Etheric Vitality Meditation (chapter 9) for personal use as taught in Levels Two and Four of the HT training program. Many variations are possible, of course, since basic principles of personal intention are most important.

As always, start with centering and setting intention toward the client—in this case, yourself—for the Highest Good. Invite thoughts and feelings of appreciation for each body area as you lovingly touch yourself. Many students and practitioners hold each area for approximately one minute, but you can hold each center for as long as it feels right for you, based on the amount of time you have from a practical point of view, or based on your inner knowing.

Exercise 13.2. Self Chakra Connection

1. *After sensing the flow of energy from the Universal to your heart and hands, bring the hands to one of the feet, holding above and below the sole of the foot. Hold until the foot feels warm and cared for.*

2. *While holding the sole of the foot with one hand, move the other hand to the ankle and feel the vibration of fullness between the hands.*

3. *While holding the ankle with one hand, move the other hand to the knee and feel the energy flowing between the two joints.*

4. *Then connect the knee and the hip and feel the sense of fullness in the upper leg.*

5. *Repeat the same pattern on the other leg starting at the sole of the foot.*

6. *Hold both hips, feeling the flow of energy between your hips and in your lower body.*

7. *Connect the root and sacral chakras. Sense the flow of energy between them.*

8. *Connect the sacral and solar plexus chakras. Move the lower hand to the spleen area to nourish spleen and pancreas energetically.*

9. *Connect the solar plexus and the heart center. Then move the lower hand to above the heart while keeping the other hand on the heart.*

10. *Connect both wrists; then connect both elbows.*

11. *Hold both shoulders; give yourself a loving hug!*

12. *Connect the heart to the high heart and then the throat chakra,*

13. *Connect the throat chakra and the brow.*

14. *Then connect the brow and the crown.*

15. *Finally, connect the crown chakra to the transpersonal point, which reaches to the Universal Energy Field.*

16. *Let your whole being extend beyond your body to sense your expanded biofield!*

This is a wonderful self-care exercise to do early in the morning to get ready for the day. It can be a quick pick-me-up anytime it's needed during the day. It can also be used to prepare for sleep. In the case of insomnia, you can visualize the hand movements and imagine them moving up very slowly while breathing with long out-breaths.

Personal First Aid

HT methods are ideal for use in a crisis. Personal crises may consist of a direct traumatic event or vicarious traumatization, which frequently occurs while listening to and observing others' distress. Other forms of personal crisis include receiving a difficult medical diagnosis or losing a loved one. Community crises affect us deeply as well. Think about the national trauma of the 9/11 events in 2001, or the ongoing saga of failed financial endeavors. Even the most hardy people who deny the existence of their feelings are regularly impacted emotionally by exposure to daily bad news.

Energetic interventions for personal first aid have to be immediately available and easy to remember. There is no time to look them up in a manual or think about what would be best for a situation. I have found a series of Magnetic Passes with strong, releasing out-breaths easy to remember and effective for me. Other quick first-aid practices include sending out love and light to people in need, from your heart center, and then rapidly recentering with hands over the heart chakra to feel love and light coming into your own being. A self-affirmation can also be very helpful in times of need: While holding your hands over the heart chakra, affirm, "Even though this (name the difficult event or problem) has happened, I deeply and profoundly honor and accept myself and choose to stay in my center, to hold the light."

It is wise for all caregivers to know how to use energetic first aid. HT methods give a good foundation for knowing what to do in a crisis when others are stuck in their own fears or intense emotional responses.

HT practitioner Kathryn Koches describes her need for energetic self-care for her work as a nurse in a hard-core prison setting: "Like many, I have a 'day job' that does not include Healing Touch as part of the employment description. I rarely get to overtly use techniques that are taught in class, but I have learned that a healing presence is often more about who you are than what you do. [emphases added] I practice my own healing ritual every day before I start work. It begins as I turn into the gated entrance of my facility and follow the gently curving, mile-long driveway to the parking lot. In my car, I take a deep breath and start to sing a little song learned decades ago: This little light of mine, I'm going to let it shine … I'm not a good singer, but no one is there to hear as I pass the beautiful landscaped grounds … a gun tower, and another. There are buildings nestled behind the seemingly natural woods, surrounded by tall chain-link fences and topped with rolls of razor-ribbon. I work for the Department of Corrections inside a state prison and was hired for the ambulatory clinic, delivering health-care to prisoners. In my heart, I know, my real job is to carry the Light into a very hopeless and dark environment.

"[My] challenge is to maintain a balance between being authentic and love-filled while never, ever letting my guard down. I must never forget I work with manipulative, dangerous individuals and never forget everyone has the potential to heal. Touch in prison can easily be misinterpreted, termed 'over-familiarity,' so I practice mostly distance healing or indirect techniques such as holding a dressing in my hands and infusing it with Healing Light. I strive to stay grounded and connected. The Hara Alignment Meditation is an important tool.

"Have I made a difference? It's hard to say, as I strive to detach from the outcome and only set the intention for the inmates' highest good. There is one prisoner whose lung cancer was no longer detectable in recent PET scans. He credits a Healing Touch treatment for his remission. I'm not so sure. I believe that all healing is self-healing. I may bring the Light in, but everyone has at least a spark, even in prison. Sometimes they just need a reminder."

Methods of Personal Development

Developing the healer within is an ongoing process. It becomes a life's passion for Healing Touch practitioners and is the lifeblood of the ongoing sharing that can be seen in the more than twenty years of HT practices. Each new participant is encouraged to develop personal understandings as part of the essential journey to effective caregiving. In this section, we explore some of the most direct ways of effecting personal growth, with suggested references for your ongoing quest.

Sigmund Freud, the father of modern psychology, regarded personal journaling and tracking one's dreams as the "royal road to deeper consciousness." There is no magical pill that can replace willingness to explore the deeper reaches of the self, other than daily dedication to learning from within. Friendship with your own best friend, your inner advisor and the inner artist of your life, is the most enduring friendship of your life. Once this friendship is established, you can begin to attract more of the resources and energies needed to accomplish your goals. As reported by many practitioners, we begin to attract exactly what we need without having to please others or getting lost in false expectations.

Writing It Down

Journal writing is a time-honored way to acknowledge yourself. Your thoughts and feelings are important. Reading something you have written confirms respect for your being. Upon reviewing what you have written, you begin to discover some of the themes of your life, your patterns, areas in your life needing further attention, and, it is to be hoped, genuine appreciation for who you are.

Journal writing is a form of private communication with your inner knowing and therefore should be kept private. You are not writing to please or understand anyone else. I have found an attractive notebook helpful in feeling self-respect for my journaling. Keeping it close at hand at my desk, I can jot down ideas, insights, and dreams. Other ideas and resources[8] can help, but, above all, keep it simple so you will actually do it!

Tracking Dreams

A modern explorer of the world of dreams, Robert Moss holds that we can explore the psyche's gifts for our present lives through techniques called dreamwork.[9] In addition, we can access through our dreams insights into major life themes such as relationships, unresolved past trauma, and even the meaning of physical death.

Initially, dreams may seem mysterious because they communicate with symbols and metaphors rather than factual information. Here is an exercise to help transform dream symbols into personal meaning for your life.

Exercise 13.3. Dreamwork

1. *As soon as you wake up, write down the key words and strong feelings associated with your dream as quickly as possible at your bedside. Remember, once you change your position or get up, more than half of your perceptions will change as the conscious mind begins to come into play.*

2. *Make as many associations as possible with each of the words you have written down. For example, "animal" can be associated with your own pet, a creature in distress, your own animal nature, a power symbol, or someone with an inability to speak up. "Helplessness" can be associated with entrapment, fear, inability to think clearly, or unwillingness to see new possibilities or solutions.*

3. *From your list of associations select the ones that resonate for you or cause an "aha" of recognition.*

4. *Form the key words into a pattern or an objective, matter-of-fact statement such as "The dreamer is unable to express herself and seems unwilling to find new options."*

5. *Think how this might relate to you or someone you know. Guess at what the message might be. For example, "I might be holding myself back and need help in finding new ways of addressing a problem."*

6. *Allow a specific action to follow that acknowledges your learning from your dream in some way. Do something specific and practical such as writing the whole sequence down, lighting a candle, playing beloved music, or deciding to seek consultation about a specific issue in your life.*

Creative Self-expression

Creativity is an innate human right. Whereas creativity may include exploring art-making or poetry, the most immediate sign of creativity is interest in being of service to others and finding meaning through our life's work. Creativity is closely linked to personal health because, unless we tend to the creative fire within, we will not have the energy, vitality, and inventiveness needed to actualize our chosen life's purpose.[10]

There are many resources for activating personal creativity, but the most vital are to commit to the adventure of daily learning while letting go easily of impediments and integrating your ideas to establish your personal philosophy of healing. Research shows that the traits of truly creative people include some of the following:[11]

- Resilience and persistence—staying power toward mastery of new information

- Curiosity—willingness to open to new possibilities

- Enthusiasm—relishing the adventure of exploring new dimensions of oneself

- Embracing the unknown or mysterious in life

- Recognizing feedback—paying attention to things that work well and those that don't

- Taking charge of one's schedule to have time for deepening meditation and exploring something forgotten

- Organizing the household to find things easily and have time to think

- Developing other aspects of the personality—overly rational people need to increase higher sense perceptions; very intuitive people need to become more adept in linear skills such as computer facility or scientific thinking

- Consciously choosing to enjoy each moment fully, being in "the flow"

- Transforming negativity into opportunity for learning

You may notice which of these qualities resonate with you, as if to say, "I would like to have more of that trait." Follow your inclination with a creative plan so that you begin to express your being in the world more actively. Studies show that brain cells are activated and regenerate with novelty and active engagement[12] so each step toward enriching your life is rewarded with increased health and well-being.

Recently, I was on a book tour to a city I did not know to speak at an unknown venue. The designated bookstore was in a dark basement, overcrowded with books and room only for a few chairs. The moment I entered I thought, "Uh-oh! I hope none of my friends see me presenting here." I recognized the negativity of my first thought and decided to reframe it by saying inwardly, "Well, maybe I can have a good time anyway. It's OK to have fun." After this, three dear friends I had not seen in years entered. Rickety folding chairs were found for them and my presentation continued. At the end, all the participants raised thoughtful questions and bought copies of my books. We had a great time and I felt supported by the universe in my adventure, despite its seeming challenges.

We can choose again and rethink our old ways of responding. Exploring paths to thinking and acting creatively is deeply rewarding. As we learn to befriend the world about us, we can see more clearly the beauty of nature and the gifts of the creative spirit of the universe.

Connecting with Higher Power

Although HT encompasses people from all faiths and belief pathways, most practitioners find their own consciousness moving toward a more personal connection with Higher Power or the Universal Energy Field. The very nature of energy in our world suggests our intricate interconnections with each other and a Force greater than ourselves. Reaching out to others energetically also moves us into relationship with our center and essential spirituality.

The HT program encourages spiritual development as each practitioner chooses. Endeavors to assist others are greatly enhanced by careful attention to possible spiritual guidance or the presence of helpers.

Here is an exercise that couples journal writing with preparation for giving an HT intervention. It is an example of practitioner self-care in action to find the highest good for oneself or a client.

Exercise 13.4. Asking for Guidance

1. *Set aside at least fifteen minutes in a quiet place to center yourself, with your journal and pen nearby.*

2. *Write down your questions or concerns either for your own well-being or that of a specific client, relationship, or situation. Identify the most central issue.*

3. *Allow your awareness to lift through each of the chakras and safely move in a bubble of protection above your body, the treetops, and clouds to the deep indigo blue of the higher planes.*

4. *Ask what would be for the highest good to assist with the concern you've raised. Releasing all tensions, allow each in-breath to bring inspiration.*

5. *Allow yourself to see or sense the presence of a helper—it may come in any form, such as an animal, a color, the outline of a figure, a strong feeling, or a sense of temperature change.*

6.   *Ask your question again and immediately write down what you receive while keeping the breath steady and releasing any distracting thoughts. If the flow of information stops, ask your question again and write down your very first perceptions.*

7.   *Thank the presence of goodwill for its help. Gently move through the layers beyond your body back into the crown chakra and bring awareness again to the renewed connection, openness, and balance sensed within you.*

8.   *Read what you received without judging it. Recognize how this practice can grow as you repeat and work with it.*

With this chapter, we see how work as a HT practitioner requires full awareness of oneself to attune to others with ease and clarity. Inner work allows us to recognize our own personal material so we do not inadvertently project our own limitations or interpretations onto clients. It also fosters the recognition of hope for the healing of others in which we can be facilitators. We can safely release our personal agendas about client outcomes and allow the Universal Energies/Higher Power to bring about the transformations most appropriate for the person in need.

Chapter Notes

1. B. Dossey, *Florence Nightingale: Mystic, visionary, healer* (New York: Lippincott, Williams & Wilkins, 2000).

2. Center for Nursing Advocacy, "What is the nursing shortage and why does it exist?" http://www.nursingadvocacy.org/faq/nursing_shortage.html; retrieved April 30, 2009.

3. P. Goldberg and R. Lichtman, "Meeting the challenges of the sandwich generation," February 2009 E-zine of National Association of Baby Boomer Women (www.NABBW.com); see also their valuable blog http://www.NourishingRelationships.Blogspot.com.

4. K. Williams, "Transactional analysis—what is your driver?" http://EzineArticles.com/?expert=Karen_E_Williams; retrieved April 30, 2009.

5. _____, "Medical errors: The scope of the problem an epidemic of errors," Agency of Healthcare Research and Quality, #00-P037

http://www.ahrq.gov/qual/errback.htm; retrieved in April 2009.

6. J. Watson, *Nursing: The philosophy and science of caring* (Boulder, CO: University Press of Colorado, 2008) 82-83.

7. D. Hover-Kramer with M. Murphy, *Creating Right Relationships: A practical guide to ethics in energy therapies* (Port Angeles, WA: Behavioral Health Consultants, 2007).

8. K. Adams, *The Way of the Journal* (Baltimore: Sidran Traumatic Press, 1998); S. Dowrick, *Creative Journal Writing* (New York: Allen & Unwin, 2007).

9. R. Moss, *Conscious Dreaming: A spiritualpath for everyday life* (New York: Crown, 1996); see also R. Moss, *Dreamways of the Iroquois: Honoring the secret wishes of the soul* (Rochester, VT: Destiny Books, 2005).

10. D. Hover-Kramer, *Second Chance at Your Dream: Engaging your body's energy resources for optimal aging, creativity, and health* (Santa Rosa, CA: Energy Psychology Press, 2009), 135.

11. *Ibid.*, 142–143 with recognition to Mihály Csikszentmihályi for his extensive research about the traits of creative people; see M.

Csikszentmihályi, *Creativity: Flow and the psychology of discovery andinvention* (New York: Harper Perennial, 1996).

12. G. Kemperman and F. Gage, "New nerve cells for the adult brain," *Scientific American* 280(1999):48.

Chapter 14

Healing Touch as a Spiritual Practice

Sister Rita Jean Dubrey, CSJ, RN, MSN, HTCP/I, and
Dorothea Hover-Kramer, EdD, RN, DCEP

*Every human being has a great, yet often unknown gift
to care, to be compassionate,
to become present to the other,
to listen, to hear and to receive.
If that gift would be set free and made available,
Miracles could take place.*

—Henri Nouwen

Almost inevitably, the practice of Healing Touch brings those giving its care to a place of heightened spiritual awareness. The moments of shared connection with clients are sacred experiences. This quality of the spiritual increases as the healer matures. The focused mindfulness of the practitioner brings compassionate caring to the person in need. The interrelationships that form between practitioner and client often lift both beyond ordinary consciousness. Administering and receiving a specific HT method can be transformed into something quite transcendent and luminous for both participants.

The personal growthwork of the practitioner as encouraged and supported by the Healing Touch Program curriculum prepares the way for the sacred to occur. It also speaks to the soul: we live in a world hungry for real substance and nourishment that goes beyond the temporary achievements of a materialistic culture. The very nature of the human energy system—its vibrating, dynamic of pulsating electromagnetic energy waves affording instant communication with living cellular matrices—suggests a direct bridge between body, mind, and spirit. This energy is also the bridge between the *immanent* and the *transcendent*, the human and the divine. Thus the small acts of compassion and kindness that HT practitioners give so generously are transformed into spirit-filled experiences.

Jason's Story

Kimberly Gray has spent more than twenty-five years working in various nursing specialties and has most recently been integrative medicine coordinator at the large Tampa General Hospital in Florida. She was given special recognition via the Clinical Excellence in Nursing award for her outstanding contribution to the recovery of Jason's life and shares this inspiring example of her HT work with prayer and her connection to inner wisdom.

"Jason was an eighteen-year-old high school senior, star quarterback of the football team, and a vibrant outgoing young man. Just before the end of summer a few years ago, his life was tragically altered in the blink of an eye. A drunk driver hit the car in which he was a passenger. He sustained a severe closed head injury that rendered him in a comatose state for the four-month period prior to my first meeting with him. The conversations between the physicians and his parents remained the same: 'We are not sure if he will come out of the coma, we can never know which way it will go!' Despite this, Jason's parents kept holding on with great faith and wanted to explore every avenue of possible help. His mother sought me out to [help him with] Healing Touch.

"I was very passionate about incorporating this beautiful complementary healing modality into my nursing care and accepted the challenge, wondering how I would have time in my demanding nursing schedule to help someone who had been in a coma for such a long period of time. When I initially entered Jason's room in the skilled nursing unit, the gaunt and pale young man who lay before me moved my heart. His eyes were fixed in a catatonic gaze, and his arms and legs were contorted and flexed toward his body. A feeding tube in his stomach sustained him nutritionally. As I reached out to connect with him by touching his arm, there was no response or sign that he knew I was there. As I looked into his eyes, it was as if he peered right through me. I could sense fear in him. I thought to myself, 'Maybe he is afraid to come out because he has so much work ahead of him.' I prayed silently within myself for direction, and knew what I had to do: I invited his spirit to come out and play!

"I reminded him out loud that he would not be alone during this healing journey ... there was so much support and love from friends and family. I then did some Healing Touch interventions. At the end of my time with him, it seemed as if he was looking at me, instead of through me. I assured him I would return. I returned each time I had an opportunity ... Following my second session, Jason was tracking me with his eyes. After the third, he was blinking, once for 'yes' and twice for 'no.' By the end of the second week, Jason ... was becoming more physically mobile. Each time I worked with Jason, it was as if a flower was starting to bloom. He rapidly started progressing in his responses. I kept reminding myself that every extra moment to do Healing Touch with Jason was a moment well-invested.

"His family was amazed at how he was 'blossoming' back into a responsive human being, and this encouraged me to keep working with him as time permitted. By the end of a four-week period, Jason was able to participate with therapies and had transcended the catatonic state to walking and feeding himself. His feeding tube was removed. He still could not speak. He would look at me, strain and groan very loudly with his mouth partially open, as if he were trying to say something, but no words came out.

"I prayed for a tool that might help him with this. One day my answer came as I was listening to *Mastery of Language* tapes in my car … The tapes teach how our thoughts and words create our reality, because the cells in our body hear our thoughts and words and respond accordingly. I eagerly approached Jason with this news the next time I saw him. [I encouraged him to] think, 'I am speaking and I am healthy' and possibly his body would respond accordingly. I reminded Jason each time I worked with him, and he would enthusiastically confirm with his crooked 'yes' finger response.

"Three weeks later when I approached his room, the speech therapist, aware of the Healing Touch work I had used with Jason, came running out, 'Kimberly, come here, come here, you have to see this!' Jason was eating oatmeal, smiling, saying, 'More, more.' I laughed and told him, 'Jason, look, you did it!'

"Jason became so busy, between speech, physical, and occupational therapy, he was too busy for additional interventions with him. I knew my purpose for Jason had been fulfilled—I had invited his spirit to 'come out and play' while continuing to support him with Healing Touch. In the two-month period I had been blessed to work with Jason, he progressed … to walking, talking, and feeding himself. I had stayed centered and focused with the compassionate intention that my presence with him was for his highest good, and he did the rest of the work.

"I went back to revisit Jason to see how he was progressing, and found him in the break room with friends. He smiled and chuckled as I entered the room. Jason's friends looked at him and asked, 'Who is she, Jason, is she a family member or your friend?' Jason looked at me with his crooked grin, touched my arm with his hand, and said warmly, 'She's my friend.' Jason has returned home with his parents, and recently graduated from high school.

"I know that my choice to connect with Jason on a mind-body-spirit level, by being focused and centered … with the Healing Touch work, truly created an optimum environment for his body to heal. His parents, friends, family, and healthcare team were all grateful and supportive throughout his journey, and also learned and incorporated some of the Healing Touch techniques during their visits. This taught each person about the power of [healing] presence."

Spirituality Does Not Require Being Holy or Religious

As we can gather from Jason's story, Kimberly's practical spirituality led her to enter into a healing relationship with herself, her patient Jason, and his Higher Power. Her prayers came from her sense of helplessness and the answers came from her trust in deeper wisdom. Spirituality is each individual's unique sense of unifying mind, body, and spirit. Spirituality is about looking within and coming home to inner peace which helps to create right relationships. It is a way of being.

Two well-known nursing authors Margaret Burkhardt and Mary Gail Nagai-Jacobson elaborate: "Spirituality is the inherent aspect of our human beingness. The spiritual core is the place that is closer than our own breath, yet unlimited in its expansiveness. Spirituality impels us to seek and to discover the more of who we are and calls us to enter the depths of our own being, where we discover our intrinsic connectedness with all of life and with the eternal Oneness and Sacred Source of our being. Spirituality enables us to wonder and reflect as we see the light in the darkness, discover meaning, see Beauty, experience love, and know that we are made for Love. Spirituality, connecting us with the source of our being, infuses our knowing, Being, and doing."[1]

The center of our being is that sacred space within us—our heart center. In a peaceful heart, there are no divisions. We are totally one with others through compassion, caring, and empathy. The HT connection is above all a place of trust. It is a place where practitioners meet clients, themselves, and a sense of connecting to Higher Power. They are called to enter the sanctuary of their own being. Buddhists define spirituality as *shamatha* or "tranquil abiding."[2] The Kabbalah, the mystical branch of Judaism, teaches that the sacred may speak to you from its many hidden places at any time. Well-known physician and author Rachel Naomi Remen interprets this tradition as, "The world may whisper in your ear, or the spark of God in you may whisper in your heart."[3]

In the Judeo-Christian tradition, quotes from the scriptures help to move practitioners to the place of stillness within: "Take care you remain tranquil and do not fear" (Isaiah 7); "Stand still in silence in the Presence of the Lord" (Zephaniah 1:7); "Be still and know that I am God" (Psalm 46).

The stillness of centering in HT begins the journey to deeper levels of self-understanding. Many HT practitioners are searching for inner peace and therefore find ways of coming home to themselves through the calling to HT practice. Of the hundreds of possible definitions, perhaps the idea of coming home to oneself best defines this broad concept of spirituality.

Healing Touch as a Practice of Hope

Living within one's spirituality expands a sense of hope. Healing Touch practitioners bring a quality of hope to every endeavor with clients, with their family and friends, and in their communities. People are searching for hope in daily life and in their pain, suffering, or dying.

Mother Teresa is known around the world for devoting her life to giving hope to the hopeless. She also found that healing endeavors bring people together. Prayer and meditation are a universal human language. She wrote, "I have never found a problem with people from different religions praying together. What I have found is that people are just hungry for God, and be they Christian or Muslim, we invite them to pray with us. There is a large percentage of Muslims in our mission houses in Spain and France and they want to pray. So that is our main focus, to encourage them to pray, to have a relationship with God, however that may be, because when you have that, then everything else will follow."[4]

Healing Touch does not recommend or require a specific religious orientation or organized religious system. From the founding days onward, we have honored, respected, and accepted all traditions. Janet Mentgen's deep spirituality reflected the inner life of a person who, from her heart center, welcomed all with unconditional love.

Expressing this practical sensitivity, Burkhardt and Nagai-Jacobson write, "We integrate spirituality into our healing practice not so much by what we *do* but by *who* and *how we are* in every moment. [emphasis added] Above all, we must come to know our own center and to live consciously from this inner place."[5]

The Kabbalah tells a creation story. "When God made the world, wrote Isaac Luria in the sixteenth century, the divine light He emanated was so intense that it shattered the vessels containing it. The light fragmented into divine sparks, the *nitzotzot,* which fell to the earth. Every particle in our physical universe, every structure and every being, is a shell that contains sparks of holiness. But these sparks remain hidden in our ordinary world. Our sacred task as human beings is to uncover them, an act of cosmic restoration called *tikkun.* This we do through acts of service, prayer, loving kindness, and appreciation, whereby we attune to and celebrate the universe. We are here to heal the world by finding sparks of the divine, and in so doing we are healed to ourselves."[6]

Through Healing Touch, practitioners help others and are at the same time healed to themselves. They bring light, sparks of the Divine, to the world. People seek HT when they are suffering physical, emotional, spiritual pain. Practitioners connect with their clients in a mindful, intentional way, laying on hands, moving hands through the biofield, and utilizing the many interventions of HT. In the words of well-known spiritual teacher Janet Quinn, "[As] whole people we are body, mind, and spirit: that spirit is always about mystery unfolding and that healing is therefore fundamentally mysterious, beyond our control, and manipulation yet open to our conscious participation and intention."[7]

Healing Touch as a Practice of Letting Go

Healing Touch is a manifestation of the Divine Feminine principle. Although, of course, men are also actively involved in HTP, the feminine principle in both male and female persons is activated by the work. The feminine is the gentler, receptive, intuitive aspect of the personality in contrast to the masculine, which is the outgoing, active, dominant aspect of each person. Both are needed, but at present, the male archetype of getting things done with ego strength and human willpower is overly dominant in the healthcare field and world politics.

In a Healing Touch session, ego consciousness drops away. The healer remains present to the client with no expectations or attachment to outcomes. The power to heal is from the divine; healing does not come from human effort. Instead, HT practitioners create an environment in which healing can occur.

The well-known saying "Let go and let God" is a relevant, powerful intention that facilitates the momentum of healing. It is a concept often used in addiction recovery since addicts typically have a distorted sense of ego control. Yielding or surrendering facilitates energy repatterning to wholeness and a higher order.

Healing Touch Buddies Program

As an example, volunteers in the Healing Touch Buddies Program at St. Mary's Hospital in Amsterdam, New York, are models for letting go of ego and practicing in a spirit of service. Begun in 1998, and funded in part by the Susan G. Komen Breast Cancer Foundation, the program became an integral part of the Center for Complementary Therapies at St. Mary's. The program offers Healing Touch to women with breast cancer at any stage of recovery every month. Some women are receiving chemotherapy and/or radiation therapy, whereas others have been in recovery for more than twenty-five years. People who have completed Healing Touch Level One training can participate as volunteer practitioners. Some who have become certified in HT continue to serve. It is gratifying for me (Sister Rita Jean) to coordinate these volunteers and to read sample client comments such as: "It was like you were taking the pain away," "That was miraculous—it felt like five people had hands on me," "The stress just melted off me," and "I am so grateful for the Healing Touch Buddies Program and for all the volunteers." As the volunteers learned to trust the presence of a Higher Power in the healing sessions, miraculous changes occurred in the recipients that reached far beyond their human dreams. Recently, the humility and profound commitment from the volunteers even generated funding for the program.[8]

Healing Touch as Part of the Practitioner's Spiritual Journey

Healing is a shared process, a spiritual journey. I share with my clients by saying, "I am here to journey with you." This often brings a sigh of relief and a smile. Healing is a process facilitated through the caring relationship. Practitioners create a therapeutic presence, a respectful and trusting relationship with the client. "Healing Touch is like being cradled in the arms of God" was the phrase one of my clients shared with me at the end of a session.

Healing Touch is about mindful relationships. The practitioner brings his spiritual self to the table and becomes engaged in the healing act, which includes energetic attunement with the client.

The intention is to be an instrument for healing, always for the client's highest good. Through therapeutic presence, compassion, heart-centeredness, and a nonjudgmental approach, the practitioner facilitates wholeness in the client. One of the central teachings in HT holds that illness and healing have meaning and purpose that are part of the mystery of life. Recognizing this reality is again an exercise in trust, especially for those who want everything to be explained and laid out clearly. As we let go of our expectations, transformative changes occur.

Sam's Story

A seventy-year-old man I (Sister) will call Sam was diagnosed with brain cancer. At the end of his second healing session, he stated, with a sigh of relief, "I just forgave a man who has hated me for twenty years." Sam had not previously shared with me any hint of the pain that had accumulated during the many years of betrayal and lies from this person. During the session, I simply remained in a state of allowing, holding the light and following the energy. This is one of hundreds of touching examples that reflect the impact of holding healing presence while stepping aside for the client to have his unique experience.

****

Sam's words continued to resonate in my mind and heart as I read the words of the great mystic Hildegard of Bingen: "From my infancy until now, in the seventieth year of my age, my soul has always beheld this Light; and in it my soul soars to the summit of the firmament and into a different air … the brightness which I see is not limited by space and is more brilliant than the radiance round the sun … I cannot measure its height, length, breadth. Its name, which has been given me, is 'Shade of the Living Light' … within that brightness I sometimes see another Light, for which the name 'Lux Vivens' has been given me.

When and how I see this, I cannot tell; but sometimes when I see it all sadness and pain is lifted from me, and I seem a simple girl again, and an old woman no more!"[9]

The Spiritual Journey of Self-care

Spirituality and self-care are intertwined. A healthy relationship with self and acknowledgment of the beauty of one's divine nature increase the commitment to self-care.

Most people find it a challenge to make time for themselves! The practice of daily quiet time in the form of Mindfulness Meditation, Centering Prayer, and other forms of connecting with wisdom becomes a high priority. These practices support the practitioner in becoming a clear vessel to facilitate healing.

Exercise 14.1 Centering Prayer

Father Thomas Keating, founder of the centering prayer movement, described this simple meditative practice: "Emptying the mind of its customary routines of thinking is a process that we can only initiate, like taking the stopper out of a bathtub. The water goes down by itself ... You don't have to push the water out of the tub. You simply allow it to run out ... You are doing something similar in this prayer. Allow your ordinary train of thoughts to flow out of you. Waiting without expectation is sufficient activity."[10]

Here are the steps for the Centering Prayer Meditation:

1. *Choose a sacred word as the symbol of your intention to consent to God's presence and action within. (Examples: Jesus, Abba, Father, Mother, Love, Peace, Shalom, Silence, One)*

2. *Sitting comfortably and with eyes closed, settle briefly and silently; introduce the sacred word as the symbol of God's presence and action within.*

3. *When you become aware of intruding thoughts, return ever so gently*

to the sacred word.

4.   *At the end of the time period you have set, remain in silence with eyes closed for a couple of minutes.*

It has been my experience in Centering Prayer that one surrenders to tranquility and peace, not trying to feel or to reflect on anything. It is a time of no expectations. The chosen word helps to bring one back to center whenever distracted. "The experience of interior silence of 'resting in God' is beyond thinking, images, and emotions. This awareness tells you that the core of your being is eternal and indestructible, and that you as a person are loved by God and share his divine Life."[11]

After developing her practice of the Centering Prayer, one HT practitioner shared, "I learned to breathe, to be still in my body, heart, and soul. It's like coming home to myself."

HT practitioners are encouraged to offer their clients the option of quiet time as a daily practice. In the beginning, the time frame suggested may be five minutes, with a gradual increase according to the client's choice.

The many opportunities for self-care discussed in the previous chapter support healing. In addition, we can experience a sense of awe and wonder when we take the time to increase our awareness of all Creation.

"Glance at the sun. See the moon and the stars. Gaze at the beauty of earth's greenings. Now, think, what delight God gives to humankind with all these things. Who gives all these shining, wonderful gifts, if not God? ... The blowing wind, the mild moist air, the exquisite greening of trees and grasses—In their beginning, in their ending, they give God their praise."[12]

While doing Chakra Connection during prayer a few years ago, I envisioned each chakra associated with the Gifts of the Holy Spirit as understood in the Christian tradition. Each Gift seemed to be aligned with the purpose of each chakra:

- Root chakra—Sense of Awe at the Mysteries of Creation

- Sacral chakra—Piety, Reverence for others

- Solar Plexus chakra—Fortitude, Ability to accomplish goals

- Heart chakra—Knowledge and acceptance, Unconditional love

- Throat chakra—Counsel, Speaking truth

- Brow chakra—Understanding, Intuition

- Crown Chakra—Wisdom, Participating with the Divine will

I was able to record the Chakra Connection as a meditation that reflects the Gifts of the Holy Spirit and to share it with many students and clients for their self-care.[13]

Healing Touch for the Wounded Healer

For those who have compassion, acknowledging our wounded-ness is not a place of judgment but a place of genuine meeting. I believe we are all wounded healers. I have often observed affirmative nods and smiles from students in HT workshops when I share this belief with them.

Clients come with their many wounds. Each day is a new beginning, an opportunity to participate in peacefulness and healing. All of humanity lives only in the present moment. The here and now is the choice point, the place where one can make a difference. In what appears to be a linear lifetime from birth to death, past, present, and future are on a continuum, while the soul's journey intersects at any moment in lived time to offer deeper perceptions. The Greeks spoke of chronos time as the apparent time line of physical life, and of *kairos* time as the timeless moments of the immortal soul. The intersection of a person's life with the eternal soul and its consciousness creates the only moment there really is—it is the NOW.

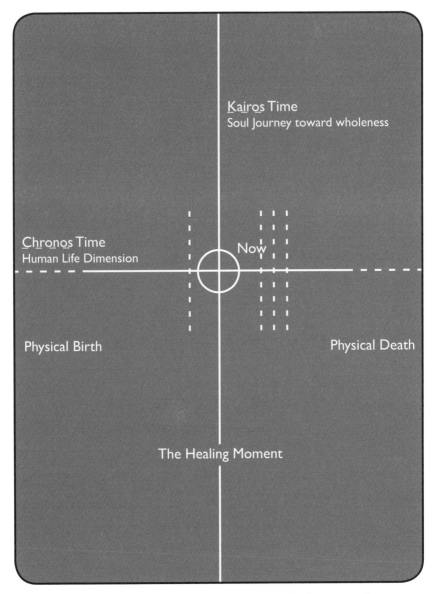

Figure 14.1 Intersection of Kairos and Chronos Time

This intersection is the healing moment. It is suspended, numinous, beyond linear thinking. It is a time of fulfillment and self-healing.

The core of the human being is immortal and indestructible. Another way of stating this energetically would be to say we are spiritual beings having a temporary human experience. By the grace of this knowing, we are absolved from fear of death as well as the fear of living fully.

HT practitioners bring the light of their being to the world as they "just do the work," an imperative they often feel and share in the face of human suffering. Practitioners offer the priceless gift of light and peace to their clients and walk with them in their process of finding their way home.

A Parable

The rabbi asked his students: "How can we determine the hour of dawn, when the night ends and the day begins?"

One of the students suggested: "When from a distance you can distinguish between a dog and a sheep?"

"No," was the answer of the rabbi.

"Is it when one can distinguish between a fig tree and a grapevine?" asked a second student.

"No," the rabbi said.

"Please tell us the answer, then," exclaimed the students.

"It is, then," said the wise teacher, "when you can look into the face of another human being and you have enough light in you to recognize your brother or your sister. Until then it is night, and darkness is still with us."[14]

The Rainbow Self

Each of the seven major chakras is associated with one of the colors of the rainbow. Through the chakras, one can connect, open, balance, and enhance the flow of energy in the body.

The following poem by Edward Niziolek portrays to me the meaning of spirituality as understood in the Healing Touch Program:

entering into positive, healing relationships with oneself, with others, and with the Absolute, the Ground of Our Being.

Rainbows are a symbolic suggestion of a person doing

everything out of love, a fully developed spiritual life

and a glimpse into what [heaven] is like ...

Rainbows tell us the whole earth is sacred and has power

and reminds us to tap into the sacred energy present

wherever we find it. ...We are all rainbows

in our own little way, in our own little land ...

Look upon the rainbow and praise the Maker.

Be a rainbow for others in the storm of life.

Chase your rainbow;

Help others find the rainbow God has for them.

Show them the rainbow that they are. [15]

We can pause whenever we see a rainbow and become aware of our spinning chakras and our vibrant energy fields. This pause can become a sacred moment for renewing gratitude for the many blessings received and the gifts of energy therapy practices such as Healing Touch.

Chapter Notes

1. M. A. Burkhardt and M. G. Nagai-Jacobson, *Spirituality: Living our connectedness* (Albany, NY: Delmar, 2001), 3–4.

2. E. Lesser, *The New American Spirituality* (New York: Random House, 2000).

3. R. N. Remen, *My Grandfather's Blessings: Stories of strength, refuge, and belonging* (New York: Riverhead Books, 2000), 3.

4. L. Vardey. *Mother Teresa: A simple path* (New York: Ballantine, 1995), 32.

5. Burkhardt and Nagai-Jacobson, *op. cit.*, 39.

6. D. Leder, *Sparks of the Divine: Finding inspiration in our everyday world* (Notre Dame, IN: Sorin Books, 2004), 14.

7. J. Quinn, "Therapeutic Touch and a Healing Way," *Alternative Therapies* 2(1966):77.

8. "SMH Center for Complementary Therapies receives Komen Grant Funding." For more information, contact the Center for Complementary Therapies, St. Mary's Hospital at Amsterdam, NY; phone: 518-841-7146.

9. E. Underhill, *The Mystics of the Church* (London: Morehouse-Barlow, 1925), 86.

10. T. Keating, *Open Mind, Open Heart: The contemplative dimension of the gospel* (New York: Continuum, 1995), 40.

11. *Ibid.*, 114.

12. G. Uhlein, *Meditations with Hildegard of Bingen* (Santa Fe, NM: Bear, 1983).

13. Sr. Rita Jean's CD is made with permission from Brugh Joy, original conceptualizer of the Chakra Connection, and can be obtained from the Center for Complementary Therapies, St. Mary's Hospital, 380 Guy Park Avenue, Amsterdam, NY 12010.

14. H. Nouwen, *Finding My Way Home: Pathways to life and the spirit* (New York: Crossroads, 2001).

15. S.J. E. Niziolek, *O Miraculous Wonder: Help us find you* (Weston, MA: Campion Center, 2008), 64–65.

Chapter 15
Future Visions for Healing Touch

Imagine a world where leaders' decisions are guided by conscious mindfulness ... a world where communities acknowledge intuitive wisdom and where scientific discoveries integrate with heart-centered thinking. If this vision resonates with you, you may want to join the many HT practitioners who already are creating such a world.

—Dorothea Hover-Kramer

N o book about Healing Touch would be complete without discussion of future directions. When my first book about HT was published in 1996, I cautiously envisioned that holistic principles of caregiving as seen in HT would become more mainstream and we would increasingly be "looking not only at the more complex ways the mind and emotions impact the body and its health, but [also] at the ways in which expanded consciousness creates a bridge between persons."[1] At the time, the core group around founder Janet Mentgen, many of whom are still actively contributing to further developments within HT, had no idea that HT would become an international force for healing and reach caregivers and clients from all walks of life. They only knew they had found a new sense of direction for helping others as they listened to their souls and followed their hearts.

This book has captured a time photo of HT in its present development in 2009 after twenty robust years of activity and growth. We have highlighted the evolution of the original five-level certification program to the rich offerings contained in the current HT certification program with its attractive, detailed manuals and weekend workshop intensives (see appendix C for a brief description of the certification program). This progression has occurred while retaining the inspired flavor of all the founders' visions. In this book, we have also considered the place of HT within the evolving rubric of integrative healthcare and energy medicine, and summarized the vast array of HT practitioners' activities by looking at their impact on various significant points in the human life cycle. HT interventions can be given from birth to death and at many life stages in between. Each contact, whether formal or informal, brings about a sense of human interrelatedness and the possibility for healing. We've also seen examples of the innovative programs that are adjunctive to HT and an overview of the international outreach programs. Beyond specifics of the HT Program, we have investigated the expanding face of healthcare, the deepening of HT research, scientific understandings of energy healing, and the theoretical base for caring interventions grounded in nursing scholar Jean Watson's prolific teachings and writings.

Public comprehension for nonlinear and nonmaterial processes has changed. Gone are the days of snickering when mention was made of the human energy system, the biofield, the chakras, or the meridians. The interconnection between body, mind, and spirit is widely accepted, and unconventional treatments are actively sought out by the growing aging population, those seeking alternative care for illness, and those suffering from long-term conditions. Many physicians now refer their patients to complementary modalities such as Healing Touch. In numerous medical communities, it is considered unethical not to respect a client's spiritual and alternative healthcare choices or to withhold information about established nonconventional programs. Healing is increasingly seen as a multidimensional and ongoing process toward wholeness at whatever level is possible for the person. Stated another way, even though a client may be dying in his physical body, his emotional, mental, and spiritual consciousness can be assisted and enhanced as part of whole person healing.

From this environment of increased comprehension for energy modalities, let's consider bright visions for the future of healthcare and specifically the Healing Touch Program. The future is as wide as our apertures of consciousness allow. Later generations will probably find some of these ideas to be much too limited in scope. For the present, let's courageously consider the following developments for the future:

- Changes in public comprehension of the physical world via innovative scientific investigations and breakthroughs.

- Changes in understanding the power of human consciousness, intention, attitudes, and beliefs.

- Changes in the evolving models of healthcare and practice.

  Here we go into a brave look at the future!

Physics and Related Sciences Will Explain the Mechanisms of Energy Healing

Ever since Einstein posited his famous equation ($E = mc2$), scientists have been studying the interrelationship between energy and matter. Current knowledge from particle astrophysics indicates the universe consists of 3–5 percent actual matter in the form of gases, elements, and subatomic particles while the rest is either a form of invisible substances that scientists call *dark matter* (approximately 20%) or invisible forces that physicists call *dark energy* (75% or more).[2] The presence of these predominantly hidden forces in the vast dimensions of space dotted with occasional galaxies can only be inferred from the gravitational effects that have been noted within galactic clusters where dark-matter halos collide with each other.[3] Even so, the presence of subtle energy within and through each known substance, including living and non-living matter, is an accepted fact. Minute, ongoing interrelationships between subatomic particles and matter are known to exist, even though they are at present too subtle to be measured. These quantum particles vibrate at different speeds and amplitudes from very low frequencies to exceedingly rapid ones exceeding the speed of light. The possibility exists that minute changes in electrons and other nanoparticles, such as those found within human cells, can influence the entire organism to make an energetic shift toward higher frequencies and hence more effective levels of functioning.

In the next decade, a definitive theory to explain how energy healing actually works will likely emerge. We may also learn more about the presence of invisible, mysterious energies that may well be present in the human organism to facilitate instant information transfers. We will understand the effects of intention on subtle energies and matter since there are already several studies confirming the influence of specific thoughts and intentions on physical matter.[4] Quantum mechanics in physics will likely lead the way in explaining the effects seen in thought-matter experiments because it demonstrates how what some call "spooky" or "weird" is, in fact, a reality under certain circumstances. Linear thinkers holding to strict cause-and-effect theories will need to accept the reality of infinite probabilities within a fluid, dynamic universe.

Having direct, scientific explanations for HT's energy-oriented methods and intuitive ways of knowing such as dowsing, penduling, and muscle testing will open the doors to widespread public acceptance. It is quite likely that energy interventions will be considered first, before other forms of treatment, for illness. Energy self-care will increasingly be a resource used by large populations of conscious people who want to stay well. Energy self-care will also be an integral part of life when the time comes to make choices for graceful aging.

Human Consciousness Will Become Understood to Be the Most Direct Influence on Health

Because of the very real changes in our worldviews due to the changing face of physics, other sciences such as biology, psychology, medicine, and neurology are also changing. Bruce Lipton's groundbreaking book, *The Biology of Belief*, has forever put to rest ideas of a self-managing physiology that functions independent of the human mind.[5] Human thoughts, attitudes, and beliefs are exceedingly powerful in communicating to cellular structures and triggering chemical reactions within the body. On the heels of this work, Dawson Church published the first popular book about epigenetics, the new science of gene expression, demonstrating again how our ways of thinking and moment-by-moment consciousness influences the expression of genetic DNA material in the cells.[6] In a nutshell, when a person is upset or holding resentments, the protein sheaths around the DNA strands tighten, thus limiting or constricting gene expression, whereas a relaxed, joyous attitude effects an opening of the protein sheaths to release genetic material and facilitate wound healing, cell restoration, and other life-giving processes.

Studies from neuroscience also show that human brain cells are much more pliable than previously thought. Neuroplasticity is currently an accepted fact for people of all ages because the brain can change and adapt to injury or new inputs with incredible resourcefulness.[7] Novelty, curiosity, and brain stimulation by seeking new learning support neurogenesis, with the building of new neurological cells and nerve pathways well into later life.[8]

Beyond these rapidly developing fields of the new biology, epigenetics, neuroplasticity, and neurogenesis, psychological pioneers including Sheila Bender and Mary Sise,[9] Dan Benor,[10] and this author[11] accept the premise that any belief, attitude, or mindset generates an identifiable energy with consequent impacts on physical cellular matrices. The consciousness of this energy can be influenced directly by working with meridian acupoints, the chakras or the biofield. The Association for Comprehensive Energy Psychology (ACEP) already exists to validate and research this work among counselors and allied healthcare professionals (see appendix E). One active ACEP member, Barbara Stone, is an energy psychology pioneer who even uses energy-oriented protocols to bring relief to persons suffering from nonlocal effects such as the presence of earthbound spirits and past-life trauma.[12]

With these rapid breakthroughs occurring almost daily, we will likely see the emergence of a new unitary science to capture the dynamic of the ever-evolving human organism and spirit. Consciousness in the form of our thinking patterns, dreams and perceptions of a cocreated reality will likely be considered the most important progenitors for human health.

Human caring and intention, so vital in the practice of HT, will increasingly be seen as the key to human well-being and prevention of disease. Human consciousness will be seen as the central focal point for understanding the secrets of a happy, healthy, and prosperous life.

Continuing Expansion of Integrative Healthcare Initiatives Will Encourage the Presence of Energy Therapy in Every Home

Hospitals, clinics, and facilities of many kinds will increasingly emphasize wellness and prevention of *dis*-ease. This shift is already under way. In many countries with national healthcare, this shift is happening more rapidly than in the United States, but the concept of preventive healthcare will undoubtedly accelerate when single-payer health programs come into reality. Energy modalities will be increasingly accepted for strengthening the interface between patients and their own learning, between healthcare practitioners and mutual planning with the patient, and between social structures committed to high-level wellness for their citizens. Prevention and early intervention with energetic methods will gain an increasing foothold not only because it makes sense but also for practical and economic reasons.

Specifically, we can envision the following developments as we live into the next decades:

- Selected energy-related intervention will be used *first*, except in emergency situations, before more and expensive invasive treatments, such as surgery and medications, are considered.

- Standardized measures of a patient's vital life force and energy levels will inform future physicians and allied professionals about the patient's status and become the basis of treatment planning.

- Death will no longer be seen as a failure in medical practice but rather as an opening to spiritual growth and higher consciousness. Caregivers including HT practitioners who can facilitate positive transition from physical life will be in great demand.

- Energetic interventions are accepted as first-aid treatments to bring about physical and emotional relief from trauma in any crisis.[13]

- One energy therapy practitioner per household will become essential for health advocacy and wellness maintenance throughout the human life cycle. Couples seeking to unite and start a family will determine which one of them will learn energy methods to facilitate problem-solving in their relationship and to handle pregnancy, birth, early child-rearing, and adolescent storms. Older couples will help each other and reach out to neighbors and their communities with various forms of energy interventions.

- The family energy field will be acknowledged and protected by its members as well as society as a whole. Family life will be seen as a sacred bond to be cherished and supported.

- Energy methods will be understood as a necessary component in all walks of life and in all parts of the human life cycle.

- Classes will abound to teach HT principles to all age groups and become part of school curricula and community education programs.

- Educational programs will lead the way in bringing the human values embodied in the HT caring model to the social fabric.

- HT books will abound, with compilations of the many wonderful stories practitioners want to share and frequent updates of theoretical and research information.

- HT outreach via teaching and healing will be part of staple energy medicine interventions around the world and will continue to increase its influence.

- And, of course, Energy Magazine, blogs and webinars will win prizes as seminal examples of media that connect practitioners and information networks.

Conclusion

The story of Healing Touch clearly does not end with this book. It is obvious that the HT community of teachers, practitioners, and newcomers will continue to grow, not only in size but also in insight and shared wisdom. The partnerships of HT practitioners and teachers who already work actively to support each other will increasingly expand caring practice and presence. This continued unfolding comes from the heart center and expands into an infinite number of possibilities for the future.

We close with a heartfelt meditation:

Feel the central core of your being

Feel the central core aligned to your Higher Resources

See the energy vortex forming around you,
stretching both higher beyond yourself and deeper within yourself

Feel the connection with a special loved person

See the energy vortex surrounding you and the
beloved person

Feel the connection with other loved ones, both near and far

See the expanding energy vortex grounded in mutual caring and love

Hear the music of their voices,

Join the intention for expressing joy and healing

Let your entire being resonate with your sense of loving kindness
and reflect your soul's purpose

Let your heart and hands reach out in unconditional caring to all beings
large and small, the web of life

Create the most powerful environment of all—

   the vibrant climate of human caring.

        —Dorothea Hover-Kramer

Chapter Notes

1. D. Hover-Kramer, *Healing Touch: A resource forhealth care professionals* (Albany, NY: Delmar International, 1996), 229.

2. A. Cho and R. Stone, "Racing to capture darkness," *Science* 317(2008):32–34.

3. A. Cho and R. Stone, "Astrophysics: Stripped in the dark," *Journal of Astrophysics* 693(2009):970.

4. D. Radin, *Entangled Minds: Extrasensory experiences in a quantum reality* (New York: Paraview Pocket Books, 2006).

5. B. Lipton, T*he Biology of Belief: Unleashing the power of consciousness, matter, and miracles* (New York: Penguin, 2005).

6. D. Church, *The Genie in Your Genes: Epigenetic medicine and the new biology of intention* (Santa Rosa, CA: Energy Psychology Press, 2007).

7. N. Doidge, *The Brain That Changes Itself: Stories of personal triumph from the frontiers brain science* (New York: Penguin, 2007).

8. E. Rossi, The Psychobiology of Gene Expression: Neuroscience and Neurogenesis in Hypnosis and the Healing Arts (New York: W.W. Norton, (2002), 221.

9. S. Bender and M. Sise, *The Energy of Belief: Psychology's power tools to focus intention and release blocking beliefs* (Santa Rosa, CA: Energy Psychology Press, 2008).

10. D. Benor, *Seven Minutes to Natural Pain Release: Pain is a choice and suffering is optional* (Santa Rosa, CA: Energy Psychology Press, 2009).

11. D. Hover-Kramer, *Second Chance at Your Dream: Engaging your body's energy resources for optimal aging,* Creativity, and Health (Santa

Rosa, CA: Energy Psychology Press, 2009), see especially the chapter on methods for changing beliefs, pp. 93–105.

12. B. Stone, *Invisible Roots: How healing past life trauma can liberate Your present* (Santa Rosa, CA: Energy Psychology Press, 2008).

13. Personal communication in September 2008. The Green Cross, as an international organization for emergency care, is very interested in encouraging energy therapy interventions and works closely with energy psychology practitioners from ACEP. Unfortunately, vested interests in New York City at the time of the 9/11/2001 disasters did not permit energy practitioners to assist in reducing public trauma reactions. Nonetheless, many ACEP practitioners worked privately with traumatized people, and one practitioner placed a full-page ad in the Boston Globe on meridian acupoint self-help methods to relieve trauma.

Note to Readers

This book represents the original work in energy healing therapy as developed by Janet Mentgen and her colleagues in 1989 and further expanded by the many Healing Touch practitioners worldwide in the past twenty years. The Healing Touch Program is the association that carries this direct legacy.

While other organizations may use similar names, they are in no way affiliated with the work, course materials or organization described in this book.

Dorothea Hover-Kramer and Cynthia Hutchison

Glossary

Assessment is the process of collecting pertinent information about the client by using observation, the hand scan, and energetic and intuitive skills to assist in planning and implementing HT interventions and case management.

Attuning is the process of consciously entering into an energetic connection with the client through the use of touch or intention. Attuning is done after the practitioner centers and grounds her/himself and before implementing HT hands-on methods.

Aura is the metaphysical term for the human energy field, or biofield, that surrounds and penetrates the physical body. It is electro-magnetic (non-material) in nature. The aura is thought to be created through the spinning and vibration of the major chakras. Each of the seven major chakras creates a correspondent level of the biofield according to Barbara Brennan's teachings.

Balancing is a term used to describe realignment of the biofield and energy centers toward its natural, highest vibrational frequencies and functions.

Basic HT Sequence: ten steps which include intake/ or update, practitioner preparation, pretreatment energetic assessment, health issue/problem statement, intention for healing/mutual goal setting, implementation of selected HT interventions, posttreatment energetic assessment, grounding and releasing, evaluation and feedback, and ongoing case planning, including attention to client's personal growth, development and self-care.

Biofield is the scientific term for the vibrational emanations that surround and interpenetrate the human body, a.k.a. the human energy field or aura (See Aura). Can be measured by SQID (Superconducting Quantum Interference Device) and is demonstrated through Kirlian photography and other instrumentation.

Caring forms the theoretical basis for HT practice and is described most fully by leading nursing and interdisciplinary theorist Dr. Jean Watson.

Centering is the practitioner's art of being fully present to the client while at the same time connected and focused within and open to intuitive guidance. Ongoing practices of meditation enhance and deepen centering. Focus one's breath assists the centering process.

Chakra is the Sanskrit term for the energy vortices, or energy centers, of the human body. Chakras control the intake and outflow of energy to specific regions of the body. The seven major chakras form an energy matrix that supports physical, emotional, mental and spiritual life and reflect developmental aspects of consciousness.

Clearing, the term used for the facilitator's hand movements within the biofield to release energy blockage, congestion or stagnation. Synonyms include: releasing, letting go, restoring flow, opening flow, or smoothing the biofield.

Chelation, a spinning out or cleansing. In medical practice, chelation releases toxins from cellular structures via injection. In energy therapies, the cleansing to release energetic blockages is facilitated by the practitioner.

Core Star represents the spiritual essence of a person and is visualized as emanating and radiating from the lower belly.

Energy blockage, general term which refers to the interruption or constriction of the natural flow patterns within the human energy system. It also can be used to describe a compromised or diminished chakra, asymmetry in the biofield, or non-polarity in the meridian flows. Chronic blockage is believed to lead to illness and dis-ease in the body-mind-spirit.

Energy center, interchangeable with the term "chakra," a specific center of consciousness in the human energy system that permits flow of energy into and out from the body. Seven major energy centers are recognized in Healing Touch, while numerous other centers exist in the body at each bone joint.

Energy healing broad term used to describe interventions utilizing aspects of the human energy system (biofield, chakras or meridians) to bring about increased human functioning. The methods include releasing energetic blockages, and repatterning, connecting, opening, balancing or aligning the energies of the person. There are many modalities of energy healing around the world, with Healing Touch being one of the most known and accepted.

Grounding the state of being connected to the earth and present in one's own physical body to feel inner calm and balance. Practitioners of HT ground themselves before and during a treatment to stay fully present and alert, and to protect themselves from temporarily taking on client symptoms. Practitioners also ground the client in selected ways, most commonly by holding the feet, to assure the client is in the "here and now" before leaving the session.

Hand Scan a gentle movement of the hands above the client's body to determine imbalances or blockages in the biofield. Sensations described during assessment may include: tingling, vibration, pulsation, stickiness, thickness, emptiness and temperature differentials. Hara Line is the personal central line that connects the human to the cosmos and the earth.

Healing the ongoing evolving dynamic of moving toward ever greater levels of wholeness in body, mind and spirit. Healing may occur in one or more of the levels of consciousness and can result in physical wellness, emotional integration, mental clarity, and spiritual connectedness.

Healing Touch is a form of energy therapy in which practitioners consciously use their hands in a heart-centered and intentional way to support and facilitate healing in as many dimensions of the person as possible. It uses intentional connection and attunement with the client to influence the human energy system by addressing imbalances or blockages in the biofield as a whole and/or within specific chakras or other energetic dimensions. The non-invasive techniques of HT are administered via the practitioner's hands to clear, energize and balance human and environmental energies to bring about physical, emotional, mental and spiritual healing. Its basis is a person-centered partnership in which practitioner and client come together to help facilitate the client's healing. Healing Touch methods can also be administered for self-healing.

Healing Touch Sequence a ten- step structure based on the nursing process that is used to guide the progression of a HT session from beginning to end. See Basic HT Sequence.

Higher Power name chosen by the HT community to define the Source of Life, Creator of All That Is, Universal Energy Field, Spirit, the One, Unifying Force, Ground of Being, and God (aka Good Orderly Direction). Students and practitioners are encouraged to integrate HT's universal language and teachings into their own personal spiritual belief system.

Higher Sense Perception (HSP) knowledge coming from beyond the physical sense of seeing, hearing, tasting, smelling and touching. Examples are intuition, clairvoyance and clairaudience. This sense of knowing comes from within and is often spontaneous and unpredicted by the receiver. The prevalence of human HSP has been growing over the last century.

Human Energy System (HES) the entire interactive dynamic of human subtle energies consisting of the chakras, the multidimensional biofield, the meridians and related acupoints, and other flow pathways. The human vibrational matrix of subtle electromagnetic energy flows is assumed to consist of aspects that have not yet been identified through scientific means.

Intention holding positive goodwill on behalf of the client for his or her highest good over and above any specific intention for healing at a particular session; focusing one's inner awareness to accomplish a specific task or intervention without attachment to a specific outcome.

Life Essence a general word used to describe the vital life force of the person and the form of consciousness that continues beyond physical life. Other terms include life energy, qi (pronounced "chee"), Ki, prana, universal energy, or spiritus.

Magnetic Passes: Hands in Motion or Hands Still, terms originating from well-known metaphysical author Alice Bailey and adopted by HTP to describe the most basic HT intervention taught. The practitioner's gentle hand movements that may be in motion or held still to bring about energetic shift from a dysfunctional blockage to openness and restoration of flow. Hands in Motion as a technique is used to clear congestion or density from the biofield, while the Hands Still method, is used to reestablish flow, energize, fill, or balance the body and biofield.

Meditation is the practice of raising the vibrations of ordinary consciousness through a disciplined practice of stilling the body, emotions and mind to become calm, centered, receptive and focused. Advanced meditative practices lead to experiences of guidance beyond usual linear perceptions and accelerate spiritual enrichment and intuition.

Method synonym for "technique" as taught in the HT Program; Levels One through Five teach approximately thirty methods/interventions. HT interventions are administered as one part of the HT sequence, which includes practitioner preparation by grounding, centering, and attuning.

Modulation of energy the process of holding the hands still over a specific area to assist in connecting, opening and balancing an area of the body or a chakra; often done after clearing disruptions in the flow of energy or qi. May be done with a light touch or off the body in the biofield/aura.

Penduling (one method of dowsing) the use of a weighted object on the end of a string or chain to assess the vitality of a chakra. Its use assists the practitioner who may have limited or unpredictable hand sensitivity and guides in the selection of HT treatment methods. Using a pendulum takes practice in order to be able to trust the results as thoughts easily influence the movement of the pendulum.

Psychoenergetic healing a form of healing practice that interrelates psychological insights with energetic treatment intervention and defines the work of energy psychotherapists.

Spiritual Practice is differentiated from specific religious beliefs or practices and describes each person's unique means of accessing an essence beyond the personal ego self. Spiritual practices include centering, meditating, praying, breathing purposefully, grounding, setting one's intention, journaling, artistic expression, learning to trust intuition and many others.

TanTien literally means the "roof of the sky" and is a term used in ancient traditions to refer to the gravitational center of the human body below the navel and on top of the uterus (in women).

Transpersonal consciousness the psychospiritual realm beyond the purely personal that reaches to the wider, spiritual dimensions of human experience. It elevates one's personal spiritual experience to awareness of one's divinity and eternal being.

Universal Energy Field (UEF) term to describe the infinite resources of unlimited energy that surrounds and interpenetrates all aspects of the Universe. This compares to the Individual Energy Field (IEF). Both terms are described in detail by Barbara Brennan.

Recommendations for Further Reading

Arrien, A. (2007) *The Second Half of Life: Opening the eight gates of wisdom.* Boulder, CO: Sounds True.

Burkhardt, M.A. & Nagai-Jaconbson,M.G. (2002) *Spritiuality: Living our connectedness.* Albany, NY: Delmar Thompson.

Csikszentmihalyi, M. (1996) *Creativity: Flow and the psychology of discovery and invention.* New York: HarperCollins.

Church, D. (2007) *The Genie in Your Genes: Epigenetic medicine and the new biology of intention.* Santa Rosa, CA: Energy Psychology Press/ Elite Books.

Dass, Ram (2000) *Embracing Aging, Changing, and Dying.* (Matousek, M. and Roeder, M. eds.) New York: Riverhead.

Doidge, N. (2007) *The Brain that Changes Itself.* New York: Penguin Books.

Dossey, B.M. & Keegan, L. (2008) *Holistic Nursing: A handbook for practice*, fifth ed. Boston, MA: Jones and Bartlett.

Dossey, L. (1993) *Healing Words: the power of prayer and the practice of medicine.* HarperSanFrancisco.

Dossey, L. (1999) *Reinventing Medicine.* HarperSanFrancisco.

Dossey, L. (2006) *The Extraordinary Healing Power of Ordinary Things: Fourteen natural steps to health and happiness.* New York: Three Rivers.

Fox, J. (1995) *Finding What You Didn't Lose: Expressing your truth and creativity through poem-making.* New York: Tarcher/Putnam.

Fox, M. (1999) *Sins of the Spirit, Blessings of the Flesh: Lessons for transforming evil in soul and society.* New York: Harmony.

Gruder, D. (2008) *The New IQ: How integrity intelligence serves you, your relationships, and our world.* Santa Rosa, CA: Elite Books.

Hillman, J. (1996) *The Soul's Code: In search of character and calling.* New York: Random House.

Hover-Kramer, D. (2002) *Creative Energies: Integrative Energy Psychotherapy for self-expression and healing.* New York: W.W. Norton.

Hover-Kramer, D. with Murphy, M. (2009) *Creating Right Relationships: A practical guide to ethics in energy therapies.* Port Angeles, WA: Behavioral Health Consultants.

Hover-Kramer, D. (2009) *Second Chance at Your Dream: Engaging your body's energy resources for optimal aging, creativity and health.* Santa Rosa, CA: Energy Psychology Press.

Houston, J. (2004) *Jump Time: Shaping your future in a time of radical change.* Boulder, CO: Sentient Publications.

Judith, A. (2006) *Waking the Global Heart: Humanity's rite of passage from the love of power to the power of love.* Santa Rosa, CA: Elite Books.

Kornfield,J. (2002) *The Art of Forgiveness, Loving Kindness, and Peace.* New York: Bantam.

Korten, D.C. (2006) *The Great Turning: From empire to earth community.* San Francisco, CA: Kumarian Press.

Kushner, H. (2002) *Living a Life that Matters.* New York: Random House.

Levine, P. A. (1997) *Waking the Tiger: Healing trauma.* Berkeley, CA: North Atlantic Books.

Levine, S. (1989) *Healing into Life and Death.* New York: Doubleday.

Macrae, J.A. (2001) *Nursing as a Spiritual Practice.* New York: Springer.

Moss, R. (2005) *The Dreamer's Book of the Dead.* Rochester, VT: Destiny Books.

Moss, R. (2000) *Dreaming True.* New York: Pocket Books.

O'Donohue, J. (2004) *Beauty: Rediscovering the sources of compassion, serenity, and hope.* New York: HarperCollins.

O'Donohue, J. (2008) *To Bless the Space Between Us.* New York: Doubleday.

Ornish, D. (1999) *Love and Survival: The scientific basis for the healing power of intimacy.* New York: HarperPerennial.

Oschman, J.L. (2000) *Energy Medicine: The scientific basis.* Edinburgh, UK: Churchill Livingstone/Harcourt.

Oschman, J.L. (2003) *Energy Medicine in Therapeutics and Human Performance.* London: Elsevier.

Page, C. (2003) *Spiritual Alchemy: How to transform your life.* London: Rider Random House.

Quinn, J. (1999) *I am a Woman Finding My Voice.* New York: Eagle Brook.

Radin, D. (2006) *Entangled Minds: Extrasensory experiences in a quantum reality.* New York: Paraview Pocket Books.

Rogers, M.E. (1994) "The Science of Unitary Human Beings," *Nursing Science Quarterly.* 2:33-35.

Rossi, E. L.(2002) *The Psychobiology of Gene Expression: Neuroscience and neurogenesis in hypnosis and the healing arts.* New York: W.W. Norton.

Scaer, R. C. (2005) *The Trauma Spectrum: Hidden wounds and human resiliency.* New York: W.W. Norton.

Seligman, M. (2002) *Authentic Happiness: Using the new positive psychology to realize your potential for lasting fulfillment.* New York: Free Press.

Spencer, R.L., (2003) *The Craft of the Warrior.* Berkeley, CA: Blue Snake Books.

Tolle, E. (2003) *Stillness Speaks.* Novato, CA: New World Library; (2006) *A New Earth: Awakening to your life's purpose.* New York: Penguin/Plume.

Watson, J. (2005) *Caring Science as Sacred Science.* Philadelphia: F.A. Davis.

Watson, J. (2008) *Nursing: The philosophy and science of caring. Boulder.* CO: University of Colorado Press.

Williamson, M. (2002) *Everyday Grace.* New York: Riverhead.

Appendices

A. Healing Touch Program Organizational Charts

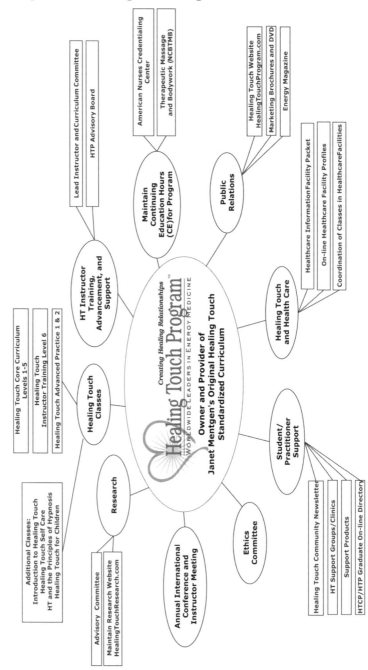

Healing Touch Program

Creating Healing Relationships
Healing Touch Program™
WORLDWIDE LEADERS IN ENERGY MEDICINE
Owner and Provider of
Janet Mentgen's Original Healing Touch
Standardized Curriculum

HT Instructor Training, Advancement, and Support
- Lead Instructor and Curriculum Committee
- HTP Advisory Board

Maintain Continuing Education Hours (CE) for Program
- American Nurses Credentialing Center
- Therapeutic Massage and Bodywork (NCBTMB)

Public Relations
- Healing Touch Website HealingTouchProgram.com
- Marketing Brochures and DVD
- Energy Magazine

Healing Touch and Health Care
- Healthcare Information Facility Packet
- On-line Healthcare Facility Profiles
- Coordination of Classes in Healthcare Facilities

Healing Touch Classes
- Healing Touch Core Curriculum Levels 1-5
- Healing Touch Instructor Training Level 6
- Healing Touch Advanced Practice 1 & 2

Research
- Advisory Committee
- Maintain Research Website HealingTouchResearch.com

Additional Classes:
Introduction to Healing Touch
Healing Touch Self Care
HT and the Principles of Hypnosis
Healing Touch for Children

Annual International Conference and Instructor Meeting

Ethics Committee

Student/ Practitioner Support
- Healing Touch Community Newsletter
- HT Support Groups/Clinics
- Support Products
- HTCP/HTP Graduate On-line Directory

Affiliate Organizations

Healing Touch Professional Association

Membership Organization

Professional Liability Insurance
Business Seminars

Cosponsors with HTP
- Practitioners Directory
- HT Community Out reach
- Elder Council

HTWF
Healing Touch Worldwide Foundation, Inc.

A non-profit 501.3C organization which receives and distributes funds to assist, encourage and advance the philosophy, objectives and methods of Healing Touch

Healing Touch Certification

Autonomous Administration of the Certification Process

Certification for Graduates of the Healing Touch Program (HTCP)

Certification for Graduates of the Healing Touch Instructors (HTCI)

B. Healing Touch Program Code of Ethics

PURPOSE:
The purpose of the following Code of Ethics is to guide the therapeutic practice of Healing Touch.

DEFINITION:
Healing Touch is an energy therapy in which practitioners consciously use their hands in a heart centered and intentional way to enhance and facilitate the physical, emotional, mental and spiritual well being of their clients. Healing Touch utilizes light or near-body touch to clear, balance and energize the human energy system in an effort to promote healing for the whole person, mind, body, spirit

GOAL:
The goal of Healing Touch is to restore harmony and balance in the energy system, creating an optimal environment for the body's natural and innate tendency to move toward self-healing.

1: Scope of Practice
Healing Touch practitioners use Healing Touch within the scope of their background, current licensing and credentialing. They represent themselves to the public in accordance with their credentials and the practice within the guidelines of this Code of Ethics; the Healing Touch Program's Scope of Practice statement; and state, local and federal laws and regulations.

2: Collaborative Care
Healing Touch is a complementary energy therapy which can be used in conjunction with traditional therapies or as a sole modality. Practitioners know the limits of their professional competence and do not step beyond these boundaries. They do not diagnose, prescribe, or treat medical conditions or disorders unless they hold a license which permits them to do so. They are credentialed and in good standing with their respective/legal licensing or credentialing body/bodies. Appropriate referrals to other health care professionals are made when necessary.

3: Intention
Healing Touch is used to promote the well being and healing for each client. Client safety, educational needs, and well-being are safeguarded by the practitioner. Practitioners working with subtle energies are careful to use their ability only in a manner beneficial to the client. Instead of trying to change

the client in any way, practitioners use their intention for the client's highest good. They use their abilities with humility, consciousness and professionalism.

4: Principle of Healing
Healing Touch practitioners know that healing is a personal, individualized process that occurs from within the inner dimensions of the client. The client is supported by the HT Practitioner in self-directing this sacred process. The HT practitioner creates a conscious, reverent, caring-healing environment. Practitioners foster an optimal condition for that client to remember and move toward their wholeness through the steps of the HT Sequence and the practitioner-client relationship.

5: Respectful Care
Healing Touch practitioners maintain high standards of professionalism in their care. They treat clients and colleagues with respect, courtesy, care and consideration. HT practitioners respect their client's individuality, beliefs, inherent worth, and dignity. They respect the client's right to be involved in their treatment and they empower the client to give feedback, alter or discontinue the session at any time. Practitioners provide information that assist clients in making informed decisions about their care.

6: Equality and Acceptance
Healing Touch practitioners work in partnership with the client to promote healing regardless of race, creed, color, age, gender, sexual orientation, politics or social status, spiritual practice or health condition. The client's inner process, spiritual practices and pacing of healing are respected and supported. No specific religious/spiritual belief or practice is promoted in Healing Touch.

7: Creating a Healing Environment
Healing Touch is provided in a variety of environments. Practitioners provide (when possible) a private, safe environment conducive to healing in which the client can relax and be receptive to the healing process. Safe and clear professional boundaries are described and maintained. Permission for receiving Healing Touch is obtained through the informed consent process. Where hands-on touch is appropriate for the healing process, it is non-sexual, gentle and within the client's consent and boundaries. The client is fully dressed except in medical situations, or other professional therapies requiring disrobing, in which case appropriate draping is used.

8: Healing Touch Sequence

The Healing Touch practitioner uses the ten-step process as a foundation and guideline, for administration of the work and in documentation. The ten steps are: (1) Intake/Update; (2) Practitioner Preparation; (3) Pre-treatment Energetic Assessment; (4) Identification of Health Issues/ Problem Statements; (5) Mutual Goals and Intention for Healing; (6) Healing Touch Interventions; (7) Post-treatment Energetic Assessment; (8) Ground and Release; (9) Evaluation and (10) Treatment Plan. Sequential order of the ten steps may vary depending on the specific situation, methods administered and flow of the session.

9: Disclosure and Education

Information is provided to the client on an individualized basis taking into account expressed needs and personal situations. The Practitioner informs the client of her/his educational and experiential background in Healing Touch and any other related credentials they hold. They also provide an explanation of the treatment to the level of the clients understanding, and clearly and accurately inform clients of the nature and terms of the service. The Practitioner discusses the HT treatment process as well as any relevant limitations or issues before HT interventions begin. Practitioners supply resources and/or additional materials that may support the client.

10: Confidentiality

 Client confidentiality is protected at all times and records are kept in a secure and private place in accordance with state and federal regulations. The Practitioner also informs clients of exceptions to their confidentiality such as disclosure for legal and regulatory requirements or to prevent eminent harm or danger to client or others. Client health information and treatment findings are documented appropriately and are specific to the practitioner's background and setting. Information is shared only with client's written permission.

11: Legalities

Healing Touch practitioners are expected to understand and comply with the laws of the state (s) in which they are offering Healing Touch as well as applicable federal regulations in regards to obtaining or maintaining a license to touch. Those that have a professional license are expected to understand how touch either is, or is not included or restricted in their scope of practice and comply accordingly. It is recommended that HT practitioners will carry liability/malpractice insurance according to state, federal and professional laws. It is expected that HT practitioners will maintain the appropriate business licenses according to their state requirements. The ultimate responsibility for complying with local, state, federal and professional guidelines is the sole responsibility of the individual practitioner.

12: Self Development

Healing Touch practitioners practice self care to enhance their own personal health in order to provide optimal care for others. They practice from a theoretical and experiential knowledge base as they continue to deepen their understanding of healing, the biofield, spiritual development, and personal evolution. They keep themselves current in the practice and research of Healing Touch and related areas and seek to continually expand their effectiveness as a practitioner.

13: Professional Responsibility

Practitioners represent Healing Touch in a professional manner by exercising good judgment, practicing with integrity, and adhering to this Code of Ethics and the HTP Scope of Practice. They encourage ethical behavior, by words and actions, to all parties. They consult a supervisor, HT mentor, HT instructor or Healing Touch Program Director when an unresolved ethical issue occurs.

****

In addition to the Code of Ethics, all students of the standardized Healing Touch Program curriculum integrate the additional detailed Scope of Practice document in their classes. The Scope of Practice Statement defines four levels of HealingTouch (HT) practice and outlines how HT providers may refer to themselves, how they can best practice, and of what they must be mindful when practicing HT.

D. Sample Forms

See HTP website for other possible documentation forms.

Healing Touch Intake Interview   Date ____/____/____

Practitioner: _____   Referred By: _____

Client: _____   Phone: _____   Date of Birth: ____/____/____

Address: _____

E-mail: _____   Occupation/Education: _____

1. **Reason for Vist/Goals**
2. **Occupation** (present, past), **Education**
3. **Experience with Energy Medicine / Healing Touch**
4. **Living Situation** (Family, Pets, Alone, Etc.)
5. **Health Care Professionals / Others**
6. **Relevant Health History**
7. **Medications, Supplements**
8. **Smoking / Caffeine / Alcohol / Recreational Drugs**
9. **Nutrition / Water**
10. **Elimination / Constipation**
11. **Sleep** (Insomnia, Aids)
12. **Stressors**
    (Scale 0-10: Illness, Work, Relationships Finances, Loss)
13. **Life Rhythm / Exercise**
14. **Relaxation / Self-Care**
15. **Religion / Spiritual Practice / Belief**
16. **Social Supports**
17. **What do you believe is the reason for your current health issues?**
18. **Anything else you want to tell me? Questions about me / Healing Touch?**

R   L

Healing Touch Session Documentation
Date ____/____/____   Session #: _____

Client: _____ Practitioner: _____

Session Length: _____ Last Treatment: _____

1. **Intake / Update:**

2. **Practitioner Preparation:**

3. **Pre-Treatment Energetic Assessment:**

4. **P.E.M.S Health Issues / Problem Statement(s) to be addressed in this session.** (Physical, Emotional, Mental, Spiritual)

```
0         5         10
|--+--+--+--+--+--+--+--+--+--|

0         5         10
|--+--+--+--+--+--+--+--+--+--|

0         5         10
|--+--+--+--+--+--+--+--+--+--|

0         5         10
|--+--+--+--+--+--+--+--+--+--|
```

R   L

5. **Mutual Goals / Intentions for Healing** (short/long term):

6. **H.T. Interventions / Treatment:**   7. **Post Treatment Energetic Assessment:**

8. **Ground and Release:**

9. **Evaluation and Feedback:**   10. **Plan** (growth work, self care, referrals, appt.):

```
0         5         10
|--+--+--+--+--+--+--+--+--+--|

0         5         10
|--+--+--+--+--+--+--+--+--+--|
```

Sample - Client Consent for Healing Touch Session

I _____, have received
information and understand that Healing Touch is a gentle, complementary
energy based approach to health and healing that can assist my body in its
natural ability to heal. I fully acknowledge and understand that this is accomplished through the use of contact and/or non-contact touch.

It has been explained to me, that Healing Touch is a complementary therapy
not intended to replace any currently prescribed medical treatments as or-
dered by my physicians nor any other medical care I have I may be advised
to seek by them.
I have been informed that my Healing Touch volunteer will neither diagnose
nor prescribe for any condition that I might have nor does she make an specific claims regarding results from the Healing Touch sessions that I receive.

I have been informed that she is not licensed to practice medicine in this
state. I have been encouraged to consult a licensed medical practitioner for
any physical or mental complaints I may have.

Some of the indications for a Healing Touch session include, but are not
limited to:
Reduction in pain, anxiety and stress
Decrease in nausea
Preparation for medical treatment and procedures and to manage side-effects
Support during chemotherapy
Supports the body's natural healing process and well being
Facilitation of would healing

I have been informed that all client information & records are treated in a confidential manner. My experiences during these sessions are confidential subject to the usual exceptions governed by State or federal laws and regulations.

My questions have been answered to my satisfaction regarding my Healing Touch Volunteer's background, Healing Touch, and what I might expect
from this session.

I give my consent to receive Healing Touch from Jane Smith, an HT Practitioner Apprentice.

Patient _____ Date _____

Parent/Legal Guardian _____ Date _____

Witness _____ Date _____

C. Healing Touch Program Certification Process

Certification as a Healing Touch Practitioner

Certification as a Healing Touch Practitioner is open to all students who have satisfactorily completed Levels 1-5 of the Healing Touch Program (HTP) coursework and received a Certificate of Course Completion. Certification is an appropriate goal for all who wish to establish a Healing Touch practice, or incorporate Healing Touch as a focus within an existing practice.

Certification is intended for the competent practitioner and requires a professional level of development. It is anticipated that individuals approach certification with preparation and work experiences that have contributed to his/her awareness of the concepts of energetic healing, confidentiality, ethics, and client/practitioner relationship.

The title granted to a Healing Touch Certified Practitioner is HTCP.

Application

Practitioner application can be found on the Healing Touch Program website www.HealingTouchProgram.com

Renewal

Renewal of certification with the Healing Touch Program takes place every five years following the initial certification.

Healing Touch Certification Review Panel

The Healing Touch Certification Review Panel operates autonomously and consists of Instructors and Practitioners with experience actively teaching or practicing HT for a minimum of two years and a commitment to Healing Touch.

E. Contact Information of Related Organizations

ACEP—Association for Comprehensive Energy Psychology
349 W. Lancaster Ave. Suite 101
Haverford, PA 19401
Telephone: 1-619-861-ACEP (2237)
e-mail: info@energypsych.org
Website: www.energypsych.org

AHNA—American Holistic Nurses Association
323 N. San Francisco St., Suite 201
Flagstaff, AZ 86001
Telephone: 1-800-278-2462
e-mail: office@ahna.org
Website: www.ahna.org

EM—Energy Magazine
5411 Villa Mercedez
San Antonio, TX 78233
Telephone: 210-653-0127
e-mail:info@EnergyMagazineOnline.com
Website: www.EnergyMagazineOnline.com

HTA—Healing Touch for Animals®
P.O. Box 632171
Highlands Ranch, CO 80163-217
Telephone: (303) 470-6572
e-mail: info@healingtouchforanimals.com
Website: www.healingtouchforanimals.com

HTP—Healing Touch Program
20822 Cactus Loop
San Antonio, TX 78258
Telephone: 210-497-5529
e-mail: info@HealingTouchProgram.com
Website: www.HealingTouchProgram.com
Research Website: www.HealingTouchResearch.com

HTPA—Healing Touch Professional Association
20822 Cactus Loop, Suite 300
San Antonio, TX 78258
Telephone: 210-497-5529
e-mail: info@HTProfessionalAssociation.com
Website: www.HTProfessionalAssociation.com

HTSM—Healing Touch Spiritual Ministry
P.O. Box 741239
Arvada, Colorado 80006
Telephone: (303) 467-7829
email: staff@ishahealing.com
Website: www.htspiritualministry.com

HTWF—Healing Touch Worldwide Foundation, Inc.
16211 Clay Road, Suite 106, Box 215
Houston, TX 77084
Telephone: 281-856-8340
e-mail:HTWFoundation@aol.com
Website: www.HTWFoundation.org

IONS—Institute of Noetic Sciences
101 San Antonio Rd.
Petaluma, CA 94952
Telephone: 707-775-3500
e-mail: info@noetic.org
Website: www.noetic.org

ISSSEEM—International Society for the Study of Subtle Energies and Energy Medicine
11005 Ralston Rd. Suite 100 D
Arvada, CO 80004-4551
Telephone: 303-425-4625
e-mail: Issseem2@comcast.net
Website: www.issseem.org

NH-PAI—Nurse Healers-Professional Associates, International
  Box 419
  Craryville, NY 12521
  Telephone: 518-325-1185
  e-mail: nh-pai@therapeutic touch.org
  Website: www.therapeutictouch.org

WCSI—Watson Caring Science Institute
  4450 Araphoe Ave., Suite 100
  Boulder, CO 80303
  Website: www.watsoncaringscience.org

Index